The Diabetic Gourmet

The Diabetic Gourmet

A DOCTOR'S GUIDE FOR THE DIABETIC, WITH RECIPES AND INFORMATION APPLICABLE FOR GOOD EATING HABITS FOR THE ENTIRE FAMILY

ANGELA J. M. BOWEN, M.D.

Member, American Diabetes Association Committee on Information for Diabetes
Consultant in Diabetes
Washington State Health Department
Olympia, Washington
Past President
Washington Diabetes Association
Seattle, Washington

with illustrations by Mary Pinckney Ferguson

HARPER & ROW, PUBLISHERS
New York, Hagerstown, San Francisco, London

 Printed in the United States of America. For information address Harper & Row, Publishers, Inc., 10 East 53rd Street, New York, N.Y. 10022.

LIBRARY OF CONGRESS CATALOG CARD NUMBER: 73-95943

75 76 77 78 79 10 9 8 7 6

Contents

Preface

Housewives and mothers bear significant responsibility for maintaining the health of their families. This is true even when all members are in good health and are permitted unlimited variety in their diets. The homemaker in a household that includes a patient bears an even greater responsibility than most, and unless she has had special training in nutrition it is unlikely that she can cope with this responsibility without help. This book is an attempt to give aid to these homemakers and so suggest other avenues of assistance.

Although many advances have been made in the care of the diabetic patient, diet is still the mainstay of treatment, and these diets unfortunately require more thought and planning than the usual family meal. I believe, however, that a well-planned diet for the diabetic can and should be a meal the entire family can enjoy. This is true regardless of which member has diabetes.

All blood relatives of diabetics have a higher than average risk of developing the disorder at some time in their lives. If this is a parent-child relation, the risk is much greater. For this reason families of diabetics should avoid excessive consumption of sugar and fat. Certainly there is no need to weigh or measure food for the nondiabetic family members, but the basic meal plan for the diabetic is a balanced diet and indeed is often superior to what the family eats if allowed free choice. How much simpler life is for children who become diabetic if they have already been taught proper eating habits!

All recipes are oriented toward family meal plans, and the use of exchange lists is stressed. Although weights are included in most recipes for those requiring this kind of strict control, it is hoped they will not prove confusing to those who have not been taught this method. The headings **C, P,** and **F** which appear with most recipes, refer to carbohydrate, protein, and fat content of the individual ingredients. Ignore them if they are not applicable to your diet.

In combination recipes where insignificant amounts of **C, P,** or **F** appear, these figures are deleted. They are likewise absent from those recipes composed of a single major ingredient; for example, a marinated roast where the marinade is discarded.

Because of current interest in the relation of saturated fat consumption to atherosclerosis, much effort has been expended to provide recipes and meal plans which utilize unsaturated fat. The fish, shellfish, and fowl recipes are especially recommended in this regard.

Olympia, Washington

A.J.M.B

Acknowledgements

Many recipes included here were contributed by diabetic patients and their families. Where possible, credit is given along with the recipes. However, many were given to me long before the thought of this book was present and their sources since forgotten.

I am grateful to Mrs. Dorothy Rockwell, my dietitian, for her generous expenditure of time and effort to double check the calculations and for her helpful suggestions. Mrs. Mary Pinckney Ferguson, Executive Secretary of the Washington Diabetes Association, provided the illustrations and also many helpful suggestions.

Nutritionists from the Diabetes and Arthritis Section of the United States Public Health Service reviewed the manuscript in its early stages and suggested numerous changes which were implemented and a few which were not. Their help is greatly appreciated.

A.J.M.B.

The Diabetic Gourmet

CHAPTER 1

Types of Diabetic Diets

Numerous variations of the diabetic diet have evolved through the years. Each has a special application. For persons with very mild diabetes, mild restrictions are applied. An overweight person with mild diabetes may need calorie restriction in addition to carbohydrate restriction. In some cases, only the type of dietary fat is changed, but in others the amount as well as the type of fat must be closely controlled. A person with severe juvenile-type diabetes may be required to weigh all food taken. In other words, a diet prescription is a very individual thing, and your physician will have taken many factors into account before prescribing. It is therefore vital that you abide by the pattern set up for you and not be tempted by what may seem a simpler program than your own. The apparently simpler diet may cause more trouble in the end. Most of the recipes included here give allowances for both weighed and exchange diets. I have stressed the use of more polyunsaturated fat where possible; if you are permitted fats that are more saturated, these, of course, may be used instead.

SUGAR-FREE DIET

This is the simplest of the diabetic diets in general use and is limited to persons with very mild diabetes, the elderly, and those nondiabetics thought to have an extremely high risk of developing the disease. In its purest form, a sugar-free diet is simply one that avoids all sugar. Pure sugar is a kind of *carbohydrate* that is quickly absorbed into the blood stream. If taken in significant amounts it can cause rapid changes in the blood sugar level and considerable distress to one's physician! All sugar requires insulin in order to be used by the body, and therefore its ingestion imposes a strain upon the person who can make only a limited amount of insulin. Carbohydrates, other than simple sugar, are not ordinarily limited in a sugar-free diet. Flour is an example of a complex carbohydrate that may be taken by a person on a sugar-free diet. Flour must be broken down by intestinal enzymes and is consequently absorbed more slowly than sugar. This permits the person with limited insulin to cope with it more effectively.

ALTERED-FAT DIETS

There has been, and continues to be, such a wide difference of opinion among medical groups concerning dietary fat that a prudent person hesitates to write about the subject. It must be difficult for the patient to understand how such wide differences continue to prevail, but there are, of course, reasons. For example, our knowledge of the clinical spectrum of disorders of fat metabolism is not even yet complete. There are at *least* three fats of importance in human disease: cholesterol, triglycerides, and phospholipids. Abnormal states generally involve too much of the first two and too little of the last. These disorders occur singly and in combination with each other. If they occur in combination, a diet that will help one may not necessarily affect the other. When one or more accompanies a disease such as diabetes, the picture is incredibly complicated. To determine the effect of various diets on these conditions is the most difficult kind of research. It is necessary to rigidly control the food intake of large numbers of patients with these disorders. Assuming that one can find large numbers of patients so afflicted who are willing to participate in a research study, one must then make repeated chemical studies of the blood before and during the experimental diets. These diets are often radical departures from the patient's usual intake. Patients who don't understand what they are to eat or tire of the experimental program and lapse into old eating patterns will produce unreliable results and perhaps cause erroneous conclusions to be drawn from the study. Thus, it is understandable that one investigator finds that elimination of dietary cholesterol lowers blood cholesterol, while another finds no effect. In the day-to-day care of patients, the physician must be cognizant of the possible discrepancies in such studies and must improvise for *each patient* an individual program that will work for that particular patient. It cannot be otherwise when even basic mechanisms are not understood. By monitoring the fat (cholesterol, triglycerides, etc.) content of your blood in response to your prescribed diet, your physician will be able to replace certain items in your diet that cause undesirable changes. Likewise, you may be permitted certain items that are generally forbidden if you have no harmful response to them. An altered-fat diet then is a highly personal thing that is difficult to generalize about in a brief presentation such as this. The principles outlined below touch on the practical problems and potential pitfalls in altered-fat diets, whatever their composition.

There are two general types of altered-fat diets. In one the total amount of fat is limited (limited-fat diet); in the other (unsaturated- or polyunsaturated-fat diet), only the kind of fat is changed. These two diets are used in very different situations and thus must be considered separately here. Excellent booklets are available on request from your physician to the American Heart Association.

UNSATURATED-FAT DIET

Unsaturated fat has assumed increased importance in recent years, with respect both to diabetes and to many other disorders. It is now necessary for housewives to be able to distinguish between saturated and unsaturated fat in the marketplace. Several generalizations can be made here. As with all good rules, there are exceptions to these generalizations, and the exceptions must be learned as well as the rules.

Rule 1. If the fat is solid at room temperature, it is probably saturated. For example, butter retains its shape at room temperature and is quite saturated, while polyunsaturated margarines that are "so soft they come in a boat" are generally quite unsaturated and indeed can be spread easily when frozen. Can we then assume that any fat which is liquid at room temperature is unsaturated? Not quite. A surprising exception is olive oil.

It is also wise to read labels to determine if saturated fats, called "hydrogenated" fats, have been added to the product. For instance, peanut butter which contains only salt and peanuts is much superior to those with "*hydrogenated* vegetable oil" added. When buying margarine, choose one with liquid safflower, corn, or soybean oil listed *first* in the list of ingredients. Because government labeling standards require that ingredients be listed in the order of greatest amount, margarines with liquid oil listed first have to contain at least 50 percent of that liquid oil. If you have questions concerning the *amount* of unsaturated fat in a product, write to the manufacturer. At present, labeling standards require information only about the *kinds* of fats.

Remember that unsaturated fat becomes rancid much sooner than saturated or hydrogenated fat (which is the reason for hydrogenation). Therefore, it is best to refrigerate unsaturated products if they are to be kept for any length of time.

Rule 2. Fats of animal origin are generally saturated. Fish is a striking exception to this rule. Perhaps the unsaturation of their fat accounts for their mobility in extremely cold water. Pork, beef, and mutton contain primarily saturated fat. Fowl generally has little fat that is eaten and can, for practical purposes, be considered to have a low fat content (assuming the skin is not eaten).

Rule 3. Fats of vegetable origin are usually unsaturated. Olive oil and coconut oil are exceptions. Coconut oil is in more products than you may realize. When "vegetable oil" only is mentioned on a label, and the *exact kind of oil* is not named, assume that it is coconut oil! Other commercially available oils vary in the amount of unsaturated fat they contain. The most unsaturated (or polyunsaturated) oil is safflower. This is an excellent oil to use in salad dressings, casseroles, and baked products. Corn oil is the second most unsaturated oil and is superior for frying foods, as it prevents sticking better than safflower oil. Soybean oil is the third most unsaturated oil, followed by cottonseed and peanut oils.

Blood cholesterol comes from two general sources: the cholesterol present in foods we eat and that manufactured in our own body from other fats. Of these two sources the latter is much more important. Should we then omit all foods that contain much cholesterol? Not necessarily. Many disorders of fat metabolism are not measurably affected by eliminating all cholesterol from the diet. Others are affected. This must be determined on an individual basis. Unfortunately, strong statements, both pro and con, abound in medical and lay literature. The practicing physician is perhaps the best qualified to moderate these extremes, as he applies them daily and notes that sometimes they work and sometimes they do not. Unfortunately, there are no definite answers at this time.

Many physicians feel that the fat allotment in the diets of all diabetics should consist only of highly unsaturated fat. Although this feeling is not universal, the fat allotment in all diets should include some unsaturated fat, preferably at least as much unsaturated as saturated fat. Stricter diets will require that at least 80 percent of fat calories be unsaturated. This is not the typical American diet, and if you are required to adhere to such a program many changes will be in store! Such a diet will require special help from a dietitian or a nutritionist.

LIMITED-FAT DIET

In the case of overweight diabetics and those with associated disorders, the total amount of fat permitted may be extremely limited. These diets require little special instruction, but a great deal of special meal planning. Often the entire daily allowance will be used in the meats eaten and no additional fat can be added.

EXCHANGE DIETS

Exchange diets are the most commonly used because they are simple and require a minimum of calculation. The basic lists were compiled years ago in a joint effort of the American Diabetes Association, the American Dietetic Association, and the Chronic Disease Division of the United States Public Health Service. Many variations have evolved through the years, but all are basically similar. One variation is included here as Table 1.

Major foodstuffs have been categorized according to the amount of carbohydrate, protein, and fat they contain. It is wise to remember that the stated content represents an average value. Thus when individual items are compared with food tables, there may be some discrepancy. These variations are minor and should be of no practical concern.

The following example illustrates use of the exchange system:

Prescription	Sample menu	Sample menu
2 meat exchanges	2 eggs	2 ounces Canadian bacon
1 bread exchange	1 slice toast	½ cup oatmeal (with)
1 fruit	½ cup orange juice	2 tablespoons raisins
1 milk	1 cup milk	1 cup milk
1 fat	1 slice bacon	2 tablespoons light cream for cereal coffee

Generally your diet prescription will include a given number of meat, milk, fruit, vegetable, and bread exchanges. It should also include some suggestions for the distribution of these exchanges throughout the day, as this will influence their effect. It is beyond the scope of this book to teach the exchange system to previously uninstructed patients. If you have this kind of diet and do not clearly understand how to use it, request help from your physician or a consulting dietitian.

Note that one exchange does not necessarily equal one serving. When you consult your exchange list always note the amount of food permitted for one exchange. Complete lists are included in Table 1.

Vegetables are divided into two general categories. Group A vegetables contain little carbohydrate, protein, or fat, and if eaten raw may be used as desired. If cooked, 1 cup is allowed per exchange. Group B vegetables contain approximately 7 grams of carbohydrate, 2 grams of protein, and 35 calories in a ½-cup (one exchange) serving.

A fruit exchange varies in amount depending upon the kind chosen. Each fruit exchange supplies 10 grams of carbohydrate and 40 calories.

Each bread exchange contains about 15 grams of carbohydrate, 2 grams of protein, and 70 calories. Note that cereals, crackers, beans, peas, potatoes, and similar foods are included with the bread exchanges. Portions vary.

Each meat exchange supplies approximately 7 grams of protein, 5 grams of fat, and 75 calories. Eggs, cheese, and peanut butter are included in this list. Portions, of course, vary.

One fat exchange supplies about 5 grams of fat and 45 calories. Butter, bacon, cream, salad dressings, nuts, olives, and avocados are included in this list because of their high fat content. No allowance is made for the carbohydrate and protein content of the nuts because small amounts are usually eaten. If large amounts are eaten regularly, your dietitian or physician will need to adjust the remainder of your diet accordingly. The exact content of most nuts is included in Table 2.

Each milk exchange supplies approximately 12 grams of carbohydrate, 8 grams of protein, 10 grams of fat, and 170 calories. Note adjustment for skim milk in exchange lists.

WEIGHED DIET

This is the most demanding of all diabetic diets and is usually limited to those who must exercise maximum caution in the amount of carbohydrate they eat. Special instruction must be given to any patient who must use this kind of diet. A working knowledge of the exchange system will greatly simplify the adaptation to a weighed diet, but, in addition, one must purchase and know how to use a good food scale which weighs in grams. The gram is a very small unit of measure, roughly equal to 1/30 ounce. For example, there are 5 grams of fat in 1 teaspoonful, or 5 grams, of oil. Virtually all weighed diets use this system of measure. Properly used, the weighed diet can contribute significantly to good health in persons whose diabetes is hard to control. Many overweight persons with only mild diabetes would also do well to learn this system and use it until their weight approaches normal. The weighed diet actually permits the greatest flexibility in meal planning because the carbohydrate, protein, and fat content of each component is known. It is therefore possible to manipulate any recipe if the principles of the weighed diet are understood. This is its primary advantage.

Homemakers who enjoy creating and revising recipes will usually prefer the weighed diet approach. These principles are simpler to apply to casseroles and other mixed dishes than are exchange principles.

Weighed diets are not simple, and individual instruction by a dietitian will be necessary. The principles outlined here will not suffice without additional instruction which takes individual problems into account.

Liquid food, such as milk, can generally be measured accurately in a standard measuring cup. Breads, meats, vegetables, and other foods must be weighed. Only the edible portion of food should be weighed. Excess fat and bones should be removed from meat before weighing. Peelings and seeds should be removed from fruit. Food tables generally give values for cooked foods and note exceptions.

Your diet prescription will include the total grams of carbohydrate, protein, and fat permitted each day. A 1500-calorie-diet prescription might permit 150 grams of carbohydrate, 70 grams of protein, and 70 grams of fat for the entire day. A sample menu is shown below.

	C	P	F
2 eggs	0	14	10
1 slice toast (25 grams)	15	2	0
1 teaspoon margarine (5 grams)	0	0	5
1 cup skim milk (240 grams)	12	8	0
Orange juice (100 grams)	10	0	0
	37	24	15

It must be emphasized here that 150 grams of carbohydrate does not mean 150 grams of food. It means a quantity of food which will supply 150 grams of carbohydrate. The same is, of course, true for protein and fat. Note in the example above that the slice of toast weighs 25 grams, but it supplies 15 grams of carbohydrate and 2 grams of protein for a total of 17 grams. The difference (25 minus 17) represents water and indigestible fibers. The carbohydrate, protein, and fat content of various foods can be determined from the food content lists (Table 2).

Patients are rarely well enough instructed to use this system to its fullest potential. A good dietitian can be most helpful to patients on such a program.

All diabetic diets share only one factor: They all require restriction of carbohydrate intake, especially sugar. Therefore, all foods which contain large amounts of carbohydrate, whether as sugar or as starch, must be weighed or measured very carefully. The higher the carbohydrate content, the more carefully the food must be measured.

UNDERSTANDING YOUR DIET

In my experience, the area of greatest insecurity for most newly diagnosed diabetics involves their diet. Many elderly diabetics eat the same boring menu over and over because they are hesitant to experiment with the exchange lists. This probably reflects a lack of understanding of basic principles. If you do not fully understand the diet recommended for you, and if your physician cannot take the time to explain it so that you do understand it, then seek help elsewhere. Large towns have an abundance of well-trained dietitians, many of whom do consulting work. Their fees are reasonable; they are expert in this field, and are often good teachers. Each state has a chapter of the American Dietetic Association. The dietitian at your local hospital is probably a member and could perhaps direct you to someone who would help with your diet or could at least furnish the address of the American Dietetic Association. County and state health departments have well-trained nutritionists who will either help you themselves or recommend someone who will. The American Diabetes Association has branches in most states (see Appendix). These associations vary widely in the services they render, but many have consulting dietitians who are willing to give dietary help.

TABLE 1. DIET EXCHANGE LISTS

In planning meals with diet exchanges, foods are divided into six groups. The foods in any one exchange group have approximately the same food values and may be substituted or exchanged for each other. The exchange groups and their food values are as follows:

Exchange list no.	Type	Amount	Weight (grams)	Content of one exchange (grams of carbohydrate, protein, fat; total calories) C	P	F	Calories
1	Milk	1 cup	240	12	8	10	170
2A	Vegetable	½–1 cup	100	Minimal			
2B	Vegetable	½ cup	100	7	2		35
3	Fruit	1 serving	Varies	10			40
4	Bread	1 slice	25	15	2		70
5	Meat	1 ounce	30		7	5	75
6	Fat	1 teaspoon	5			5	45

It is important that the food values of the diet be kept constant. The substitution of one food for another is often necessary and frequently convenient. The following lists will serve as a guide.

LIST 1: MILK EXCHANGES

(carbohydrate, 12 grams; protein, 8 grams; fat, 10 grams; calories, 170)

	Measure	Grams
Buttermilk*	1 cup	240
Milk, evaporated*	½ cup	120
Milk, powdered, instant*	⅓ cup	25
Milk, skim*	1 cup	240
Milk, whole	1 cup	240

* Two fat exchanges, or 85 calories, are "saved" if milk is "fat-free."

LIST 2A: VEGETABLE EXCHANGES

(contain little carbohydrate, protein, or calories; often referred to as *3 percent vegetables,* as that is approximate amount of carbohydrate they contain; need not be counted in amounts up to 1 cup, except tomatoes, which are limited to ½ cup)

Asparagus
Beans, string and wax
Broccoli
Brussels sprouts
Cabbage
Cauliflower
Celery
Chicory
Chives
Cucumbers
Eggplant

Escarole
Greens:
- Beet greens
- Chard, Swiss
- Collards
- Dandelion
- Kale
- Mustard
- Romaine
- Spinach
- Turnip greens

Lettuce
Mushrooms
Okra
Parsley
Peppers
Radishes
Sauerkraut
Squash, summer
Tomatoes or juice
V-8 cocktail vegetable juice
Water cress

LIST 2B: VEGETABLE EXCHANGES

(carbohydrate, 7 grams; protein, 2 grams; calories, 35; often referred to as *7 percent vegetables,* as that is approximate amount of carbohydrate they contain; one serving is ½ cup or 100 grams)

Artichoke, French
Beets
Carrots or juice
Celery root
Kohlrabi

Onions
Peas, green
Pumpkin
Rutabagas
Salsify (oyster plant)

Squash, winter
Tomato purée, canned
Turnips
Vegetables, frozen, mixed

LIST 3: FRUIT EXCHANGES

(carbohydrate, 10 grams; calories, 40)

	Measure	Grams
Apple	½ medium	75
Apple juice	⅓ cup	80
Applesauce	½ cup	100
Apricots, dried	4 halves	20
Apricots, fresh or canned	2 medium	100
Banana	½ small	50
Berries (strawberries, raspberries, blackberries)	¾ cup	100
Blueberries	½ cup	65
Cantaloupe (6 inches in diameter)	¼	200
Cherries	10 large	65
Dates	2	15
Figs, dried	1 small	15

	Measure	Grams
Figs, fresh	2 large	50
Fruit cocktail, canned	½ cup	100
Grapefruit	½ small	100
Grapefruit juice	½ cup	100
Grapes	12 large	65
Grape juice	¼ cup	60
Honeydew melon (7 inches in diameter)	⅛	200
Mango	½ small	65
Nectarine	1 small	60
Orange	1 small	100
Orange juice	½ cup	100
Papaya	⅓ medium	100
Peach	1 medium (½ cup)	100
Pear	1 small (½ cup)	100
Pineapple	½ cup	80
Pineapple juice	⅓ cup	80
Plums	2 small	100
Prunes, dried	2 medium	25
Prune juice	¼ cup	60
Raisins	2 tablespoons	15
Tangerine	1 large	100
Watermelon	1 cup	200

LIST 4: BREAD EXCHANGES

(carbohydrate, 15 grams; protein, 2 grams; calories, 70)

	Measure	Grams
Bread	1 slice	25
Biscuit (2 inches in diameter)	1	35
Bread sticks	4 4-inch pieces	20
Cornbread (1½-inch cube)	1	35
Hamburger bun	½	25
Melba toast	4 pieces	20
Muffin (2 inches in diameter)	1	35
Roll (plain)	1 medium	25
Cereals, cooked	½ cup	100
Dry, flake, and puff types	¾ cup	20
Crackers*		
Graham	3 square	20
Oyster	½ cup	20
Ry-Krisp	3 pieces	20
Saltines (2 inches square)	6	20
Soda (2½ inches square)	3	20
Zwieback	3	20
Flour	2½ tablespoons	20
Macaroni, rice, sphaghetti, noodles (cooked)	½ cup	100

	Measure	Grams
Popcorn	1 cup	15
Pretzels (three-ring)	6	20
Vegetables		
Beans and peas, dried, cooked	½ cup	90
Corn	⅓ cup	80
Parsnips	½ cup	100
Potatoes, white	½ cup	100
Potatoes, sweet or yams	¼ cup	50

* Crackers (except Ry-Krisp) are nutritionally very poor and should therefore be used rarely.

LIST 5: MEAT EXCHANGES

(protein, 7 grams; fat, 5 grams; calories, 75; note that all items are given in cooked portion)

	Measure	Grams
Cheese (any except cottage and Philadelphia cream)	1 ounce	30
Cheese, cottage	¼ cup	45
Egg	1	
Fish (canned tuna, salmon)	¼ cup	30
Fish (salmon, cod, trout, halibut)	1 ounce	30
Lunch meat (4½ by ⅛ inches)	1 slice	45
Meat and poultry (beef, lamb, pork, liver, chicken, etc.)	1 ounce	30
Peanut butter (omit ½ fruit exchange and 2 fat exchanges)	2 tablespoons	30
Shellfish (crab, lobster)	¼ cup	45
Shellfish (shrimp, clams, oysters)	5 medium	45
Wiener (8 or 9 per pound)	1	50

LIST 6: FAT EXCHANGES

(fat, 5 grams; calories, 45)

	Measure	Grams
Avocado (4 inches in diameter)	⅛	25
Bacon, crisp	1 slice	10
Butter or margarine	1 teaspoon	5
Cream, heavy (40 percent)	1 tablespoon	15
Cream, light (20 percent)	2 tablespoons	30
Cream cheese	1 tablespoon	15
French dressing	1 tablespoon	15
Mayonnaise	1 teaspoon	5
Nuts	6 small	10
Oil, vegetable	1 teaspoon	5
Olives	5 small	30

TABLE 2. FOOD CONTENT LISTS
(In Gram Weights)

MILK*

	Weight (grams)	C	P	F	Calories
Buttermilk	240	12	8		85
Milk, evaporated	120	12	8	10	170
Milk, evaporated, skim	120	12	8		85
Milk, powdered, instant	25	12	8	10	170
Milk, powdered, instant skim	25	12	8		85
Milk, skim	240	12	8		85
Milk, whole	240	12	8	10	170
Yogurt, plain†	240	12	8	4	120

* If you use 2 percent milk, call your dairy to obtain the analysis. This milk sometimes contains 2 percent additional milk solids in addition to a lowered fat content of 2 percent.

† The fat content of yogurt varies.

VEGETABLES

Group A: 3 percent carbohydrate

(average 3 grams of carbohydrate and 15 calories in 100-gram serving)

Asparagus
Beans, string and wax
Broccoli
Brussels sprouts
Cabbage
Cauliflower
Celery
Chicory
Chives
Cucumbers
Eggplant

Escarole
Greens:
- Beet greens
- Chard, Swiss
- Collards
- Dandelion
- Kale
- Mustard
- Romaine
- Spinach
- Turnip greens

Mushrooms
Okra
Parsley
Pepper
Radishes
Sauerkraut
Squash, summer
Tomatoes or juice
V-8 cocktail vegetable juice
Water cress

Group B: 7 percent carbohydrate

(average 7 grams of carbohydrate, 2 grams of protein, and 35 calories in 100-gram serving)

Artichoke, French
Beets
Carrots or juice
Celery root
Kohlrabi

Onions
Peas, green
Pumpkin
Rutabagas
Salsify (oyster plant)

Squash, winter
Tomato puree, canned
Turnips
Vegetables, frozen mixed

MISCELLANEOUS VEGETABLES

(values given are for cooked weight)

	Weight (grams)	C	P	F	Calories
Beans or peas, dried	90	15	2		70
Beans, lima (fresh or frozen)	90	15	2		70
Corn	80	15	2		70
Parsnips	100	15	2		70
Soybeans	100	9	10	5	120
Sweet potatoes and yams	50	15	2		70

FRUITS

(values given are for edible portion—fresh, cooked, canned, or frozen without sugar)

Group A: 5 percent carbohydrate

(100 grams will average 5 grams of carbohydrate and 20 calories)

Cantaloupe
Honeydew melon
Lemons or juice
Rhubarb
Watermelon

Group B: 10 percent carbohydrate

(100 grams will average 10 grams of carbohydrate and 40 calories)

Applesauce
Apricots
Blackberries or juice
Boysenberries
Cranberries
Currants
Fruit cocktail (canned)
Grapefruit or juice
Huckleberries
Limes or juice
Loganberries
Oranges or juice
Papayas
Peaches
Pears
Plums
Raspberries
Strawberries
Tangerines

Group C: 15 percent carbohydrate

(100 grams will average 15 grams of carbohydrate and 60 calories)

Apples or juice
Blueberries
Cherries
Grapes or juice
Mangoes
Nectarines
Persimmons
Pineapple or juice
Pomegranates

Group D: 20 percent carbohydrate

(100 grams will average 20 grams of carbohydrate and 80 calories)

Bananas
Figs
Prune juice

MISCELLANEOUS FRUITS

	Weight (grams)	C	P	F	Calories
Apricots, dried	20	10			40
Avocado	100	5	2	15	165
Cranberry juice, dietetic	100	2			11
Dates, dried figs, raisins	15	10			40
Prunes, dried (seed weight included)	25	10			40

BREADS AND CEREALS

	Weight (grams)	C	P	F	Calories
Bread					
Biscuit	35	15	2	6	125
Bread sticks, melba toast	20	15	2		70
Cornbread	35	15	2	3	100
Hamburger bun	55	30	4		140
Muffin (2 inches in diameter)	35	15	2	3	100
White, whole-wheat, rye, plain rolls	25	15	2		70
Cereals					
Cereals, cooked	100	15	2		70
Cereals, uncooked, dry weight	20	15	2		70
Cereals, packaged, ready to eat	20	15	2		70
Cornstarch	8	7			30
Wheat germ	10	5	3	1	35
Crackers					
Graham, oyster, Ry-Krisp, saltines, soda, zwieback	20	15	2		70
Flour					
Rye and wheat	10	7	1		35
Soy*	10	3	5	1	40
Macaroni, noodles, rice, spaghetti (cooked weight)	100	15	2		70

* The analysis of soy flour varies considerably among milling companies.

MEAT, POULTRY, FISH, CHEESE, EGGS

	Weight (grams)	C	P	F	Calories
Beef, lamb, pork, ham	30		7	5	75
Cheese					
American, Swiss	30		7	9	110
Cottage	45		7	3	55
Eggs					
Whole	1		7	5	75
White	1		3		15
Yolk	1		4	5	60
Fish (salmon, cod, trout, halibut)	30		7	1	40
Lunch meat	45		5	8	90
Peanut butter	30	6	8	14	180
Poultry, dried beef, veal, game, liver	30		7	3	55
Shellfish (crab, lobster, shrimp, clams, oysters)	45		7	1	40
Wiener	50		7	10	125

FATS

	Weight (grams)	C	P	F	Calories
Bacon, crisp	10		2	5	55
Butter or margarine	5			4	35
Cream, heavy (40 percent)	15			6	55
Cream, light (20 percent)	30	1	1	6	65
Cream cheese	15		1	6	55
French dressing	15	2		6	60
Mayonnaise	5			4	35
Neufchâtel cheese	30	1	3	7	70
Nuts, average for all nuts*	10	2	2	6	70
Almonds	10	2	2	5	60
Beechnuts	10	2	2	5	60
Brazil nuts	10	1	1	7	70
Butternuts	10	1	2	6	65
Cashews	10	3	2	5	65
Filberts	10	2	1	6	65
Hickory nuts	10	1	1	7	70
Macadamia nuts	10	2	1	7	75
Peanuts	10	2	3	5	65
Pecans	10	2	1	7	75
Walnuts, English	10	2	2	6	65
Oil, vegetable	5			5	45
Olives, green (seed weight included)	50			6	55
Olives, ripe (seed weight included)	30			6	55

* Unless larger quantities of specific nuts are desired, use the "average" figure for nuts.

MISCELLANEOUS FOODS

	Weight (grams)	C	P	F	Calories
Carbonated beverage (sweet)*	100	10			40
Catsup or chili sauce	15	4			15
Cocoa, unsweetened	5	1		1	15
Ovaltine	10	7	1		30
Ice cream, plain, vanilla	50	10	2	6	100
Ice cream, dietetic or sugar-free	50	10	2	5	95
Popcorn, popped	15	12	2		55
Potato chips and Fritos	15	7	1	6	85
Soy sauce	30	3			15
Sunflower seeds	15	3	4	7	90
Yeast, brewer's, powder	10	4	4		30

* Use sugar sweetened carbonated beverages only in emergencies, such as illness or insulin reactions.

FREE FOODS

(the following items have negligible carbohydrate, protein, and fat, and may be used as desired)

Artificial sweeteners
Broth and bouillon (fat-free)
Coffee
Flavoring extracts (vanilla, lemon, etc.)
D-Zerta
Gelatin, unsweetened
Mustard
Pepper, other spices and herbs
Pickles, unsweetened
Rennet tablets (Junket)
Tea
Vinegar

The figures used for determining these tables were taken from *Composition of Foods* (U.S. Department of Agriculture Handbook No. 8), Washington, D.C., G.P.O., 1963, and Charles F. Church, *Food Values of Portions Commonly Used,* Philadelphia, J. B. Lippincott Co., 1966.

into the blood stream and therefore provides small amounts of energy over several hours. All proteins contain about 4 calories per gram or 115 calories per ounce.

FAT

Fat, unfortunately, needs little introduction to the majority of Americans. Chemically, fat is composed of fatty acids held together by a common bond. Fat causes no fluctuation in the blood sugar level, and its primary function is to furnish the essential fatty acids necessary for growth and reproduction and to act as an energy reserve. Most of us do not need an energy reserve nearly as large as we carry! Indeed, unless large amounts of energy are expended in physical exercise, the amount of fat in the diet must be watched with care. In middle-aged and older individuals this is especially true. Many older people will have very limited fat allowances in their diets, and consequently, the fat allowed must be of the highest nutritional quality. Since vegetable fats contain much higher quantities of the essential fatty acids than do animal fats, the former should be used more frequently than the latter. Regardless of its origin, fat contains 9 calories per gram (about ¼ teaspoon) or 255 calories per ounce. This high caloric value is a mixed blessing. While it is the downfall of many overweight diabetics, it makes a splendid contribution to the diets of juvenile diabetics and those whose disease is hard to control by decreasing the rate at which sugar is absorbed from the intestines. Indeed, if the calories from fat and protein are at least double the number from carbohydrate at any feeding, much less fluctuation in the blood sugar will occur than if the carbohydrate is taken alone. This is of immense practical importance to the diabetic who has extreme difficulty in maintaining a stable blood sugar level. Fat also provides much needed calories for active teenagers.

In addition to protein, fat, and carbohydrate, many other nutrients are needed for the maintenance of health. These can be considered in two general categories: minerals and vitamins.

MINERALS

Minerals include such diverse elements as iron, calcium, iodine, and cobalt. These are found in conjunction with carbohydrate and protein foods and are a necessary part of the diet of diabetics and nondiabetics alike.

There are wide differences in the daily requirements for minerals and trace elements among age groups and sexes. Growing children and women of childbearing age require more iron than do adult men and aged women. Definite requirements for most of the essential trace elements are not known. It is mechanically difficult to determine these requirements, and about all that can be said with certainty is that "some" is needed for health. Even for well-studied minerals, such as calcium, phosphorus, and iron, discussions of minimum daily requirements stir debate in learned circles. The National Research Council on Food and Nutrition periodically issues recommended levels of intake for all known essential foodstuffs, and their recommendations represent the best advice we have at the present time.

VITAMINS

Vitamins, like trace minerals, are needed in small amounts for the maintenance of good health in diabetics and nondiabetics alike. Because vitamins occur naturally in association with varying amounts of protein, carbohydrate, and fat, the diabetic must be somewhat more sure of his sources than the nondiabetic. A person who can eat as much as he wants of the entire spectrum of foods seldom suffers from vitamin deficiency. This, unhappily, is not the case with diabetics. Not only must the range of foods be limited, but also the amount. It is therefore mandatory that all calories taken, especially as carbohydrate and fat, carry their full weight of vitamin content. This is especially important if calories are limited to less than 1500 per day. There are two general categories of vitamins: those that dissolve in water and thus must be taken daily, and those that dissolve in fat and can be stored by the body for long periods of time. The water-soluble group includes all the B vitamins and vitamin C. The fat-soluble group includes vitamins A, D, E, and K.

THE B VITAMINS

This group encompasses a wide variety of compounds that are found in dissimilar places and perform a wide range of biologic duties. All are necessary in small amounts for good health, growth, and reproduction. Most come with considerable carbohydrate attached, and it is therefore necessary to make all carbohydrate foods as nutritious in B vitamins as possible. Many of these vitamins may be obtained from frequently eaten foods such as bread, but others are found in seldom eaten foods such as liver and wheat germ. Enrichment of white flour adds vitamin B_1, riboflavin, niacin, and iron in amounts which approximate the content of whole-wheat flours. This provides a reasonable facsimile of whole-wheat flour for the person who prefers white bread and who may take unlimited amounts of bread and other foodstuffs daily. Such an option is not available to the diabetic, however. In addition to the above mentioned nutrients, whole wheat contains folic acid, biotin, inositol, and para-aminobenzoic acid—all part of the B complex and all necessary for good health. All these nutrients can be obtained from other sources, but if the carbohydrate intake is limited to 150 grams per day or less, it may not be possible to obtain the nutrients and remain within the recommended amount of carbohydrate. For this reason, and because mineral content is seriously impaired by the milling process used to make white flour, the Committee on Food and Nutrition of the American Diabetes Association has recommended that diabetics use whole-grain breads and cereals.

On the other hand, one must not entirely sacrifice enjoyment of food to the pursuit of good nutrition, nor is it necessary to do so. Certain dishes do not lend themselves well to the use of whole-wheat flour. In these few dishes, then, one should seek methods of supplementing white flour without altering the flavor. This can often be done by substituting other flours, such as soy, for a portion of the total flour. Another method is to sift ¼ cup of brewer's yeast with 2 cups of white flour, an addition that increases the flour's nutritional level considerably and alters its flavor hardly at all. If such flour is then used for baking bread, crusts, dumplings, or pastries, the flavor of the yeast is entirely compatible. Some nutritionists feel the above precautions are unnecessary, but I believe this kind of supplementation is better nutritionally and financially than the multiple-vitamin tablets so widely taken.

B vitamins are found in the seeds of most plants; for example, dried beans, peas, and nuts all contain differing amounts of the various compounds. Liver and brewer's yeast are excellent sources of B vitamins. However, for most people, bread and cereal remain the primary sources of B vitamins, and we must be sure that the bread eaten is of the highest nutritional quality.

VITAMIN C

Although this vitamin is probably taken by more people as a supplement than any other vitamin, it is found in many delicious natural foods—oranges, grapefruit, tomatoes, peppers, melons, and many other fruits and vegetables. It is destroyed by exposure to heat and air and dissolves readily in water and juices of all kinds. It is added to most canned fruit juices in liberal quantities. Certainly there is no excuse for an American to be deficient in vitamin C if only he knows where to find it. The minimum amount required in the daily diet is about 35 milligrams, and the National Research Council has recommended a daily intake of at least 55 to 60 milligrams to allow a margin for error. This amount can be obtained from ½ cup of orange or grapefruit juice. It can be taken in a variety of other combinations of fruits and vegetables as well. Your diabetic diet will undoubtedly contain a specific number of fruit and vegetable exchanges daily. It is important to take these from the specified foods in order to ensure adequate vitamin C. Like the B vitamins, C comes with carbohydrate attached, and it is therefore important that the diabetic get as much vitamin as possible for the amount of carbohydrate. If your diet was planned by a dietitian or physician, provision will have been made for adequate vitamin C.

VITAMIN A

Vitamin A is used in the body for maintenance of healthy eyes, skin, hair, and nails. Diabetics have more infections which involve the skin and nails than nondiabetics, and therefore all precautions should be taken to ensure the health of these tissues. Vitamin A is found in leafy green vegetables, yellow fruits and vegetables, and liver from all animals. Your diabetic diet's allocation of foods from the various fruit and vegetable lists provides for adequate vitamin A. This vitamin dissolves in fat but not in water. Therefore, it is stored in the body for long periods of time, and if taken one day and not used it may be saved for another day when the intake is not adequate. This is in contrast to the B and C vitamins, which are lost in the urine if not needed immediately by the body. About 5000 units of vitamin A are needed daily. This amount is present in one healthy carrot or ⅓ cup of cooked leafy green vegetable such as turnip greens. It is possible to take too much vitamin A, and therefore good dietary sources are preferable to concentrated forms such as vitamin tablets.

VITAMIN D

The primary function of vitamin D is the building and maintenance of strong, healthy bones. It is required by both children and adults. About 400 units are needed daily, and fortified milk is the most reliable source, with 1 quart providing a day's allowance of 400 units. Vitamin D is found in small amounts in liver and egg yolk; these foods alone cannot supply the needed amount in most diets. Keep in mind that skim milk may not be fortified with vitamin D. If skim milk is used exclusively and there is limited exposure to sunlight, it is sometimes necessary to provide a supplement, especially for growing children. Adequate vitamin D is necessary for the absorption of calcium from the intestine; like vitamin A, vitamin D may be stored in the body for many days after it is taken. Too large a quantity may cause serious illness, and this complication is frequently seen among people who take large amounts regularly by capsule. Again, it is better to rely upon a well-planned diet than upon vitamin supplements. Vitamin D should not be taken as a supplement unless specifically prescribed.

VITAMIN E

Vitamin E is one of the more recently discovered vitamins and its function is not entirely clear. It is necessary for growth and reproduction in animals and probably humans. From 25 to 30 units of vitamin E has recently been established as the recommended daily allowance. It is found naturally in green leaves and cereal seeds, especially wheat germ. It is also present in corn, soybean, and cottonseed oils. Small amounts are found in milk, butter, eggs, and liver. Diets which include whole-grain cereals and breads, milk, eggs, and leafy green vegetables are unlikely to be deficient in vitamin E.

VITAMIN K

Vitamin K is essential for normal function of the liver and blood. It is one of several compounds necessary for proper blood clotting to occur. Deficiencies are rarely seen except in newborn babies. Vitamin K is found naturally in leafy green vegetables, tomatoes, egg yolks, soybean oil, and liver. No minimum daily requirement has been established because vitamin K can be manufactured within the body.

GENERAL GUIDELINE FOR DIABETICS

The 1967 Committee on Food and Nutrition of the American Diabetes Association published recommendations for the diabetic patient. The Committee advised that:

1. Adequate quantity and quality of protein should be taken to provide for normal growth and repair of tissues. (Protein ordinarily constitutes at least 20 percent of total caloric intake. At least ½ gram per pound of ideal body weight is needed.)
2. The diabetic diet should contain sufficient variety of vegetables, fruits, whole-grain cereal products, nonfat dairy products, and other

vitamin- and mineral-rich foods to provide adequate minerals, vitamins, and essential fatty acids. (Unless you have been instructed specifically otherwise, this can often be accomplished by taking the carbohydrate allowed as one-third vegetables, one-third fruits and milk, and one-third grain products.)

3. Calories should be sufficient only to achieve and maintain "normal lean body weight."

4. Appropriate combination of protein, fat, and carbohydrate intake at each meal or snack prevents wide changes in the blood sugar level. (This usually means taking at least one-third of calories as protein, one-third as fat, and not more than one-third as carbohydrate *at each meal or snack.*)

5. Food should be spaced to balance insulin and physical activity and thereby avoid wide changes in the blood sugar. (Midafternoon and bedtime snacks frequently help in this regard, especially if insulin is taken. Extra food before unusual exercise prevents insulin reactions.)

6. If blood fat levels are persistently abnormal, they should be lowered by appropriate dietary measures. This diet will require help from your physician and dietitian.

These guidelines are necessarily broad and sufficiently vague to permit adaptation to individual cases. Be sure that at least one food from each of the following categories is taken daily.

Vitamin A. Yellow fruits and vegetables, butter or margarine, green leafy vegetables, whole milk, eggs, and liver.

Vitamin B complex. Whole-grain bread and enriched cereals, milk, green leafy vegetables, wheat germ, liver, and brewer's yeast.

Vitamin C. Orange or grapefruit juice, fresh raw fruits and vegetables. Remember that several of the latter must be taken to provide adequate amounts.

Vitamin D. Whole milk, margarine, liver, and additives to many processed foods, including some brands of skim milk (read the lables for amounts). Bare skin exposed to sunlight also absorbs this vitamin.

Vitamin E. Soybean, corn, and other vegetable oils, wheat germ, whole-grain cereals, eggs, leafy green vegetables.

Vitamin K. Green vegetables. This vitamin is also manufactured by your own intestinal bacteria.

Calcium. Milk and cheese. It is virtually impossible to obtain the minimum daily requirement without the use of dairy products. Remember that skim milk and buttermilk contain all the calcium, and none of the saturated fat, that whole milk and cheese contain.

Phosphorus. Milk, eggs, meats, and breads.

Iron. Eggs, liver and other meats, whole-grain and enriched breads and cereals.

Essential fatty acids. Vegetable oils.

Trace minerals. All unprocessed foods. Iodized salt should be used, as iodine does not occur in some geographic areas.

Protein. Meat, cheese, nuts, eggs, milk, and soybeans.

Carbohydrate. Fruit, vegetables, milk, and grain products.

Fat. Meat, eggs, whole milk, margarine, cheese, and vegetable oil. Remember to choose fats wisely, limiting saturated fats found in whole milk, butter, cheese, and egg yolk, and including some sources of unsaturated fats.

CHAPTER 3

Meal Planning

In my experience the only system of meal planning that works is one that incorporates both my work schedule and a shopping list. A good meal planning system should save more time than it takes to make the plan. In addition, it should take into account the time available to prepare the meal, the amount of money required to buy the ingredients, special individual needs (such as diabetics have), and, of course, nutritional content.

PLANNING SYSTEM

A serviceable plan may be as follows:

Step 1. Prepare a master list of main dishes, vegetables, breads, salads, and desserts served repeatedly to your family. It is desirable to subdivide the vegetable list into exchange or percentage lists.

Step 2. Combine the above components into meal plans, considering compatibility of preparation, flavor combinations, and the limitations of your diet.

Step 3. Make daily meal plans, considering three main meals and snacks, if any. If there are days when you arrive home late and wish to fix quick suppers, or mornings when you leave early and need quick breakfasts, be sure to consider these factors when making your daily plans. If your schedule is unpredictable, prepare a reserve of quick menus that can be easily altered to complete the day's nutritional needs.

Step 4. Check food content lists to be sure all essential nutrients are supplied each day and adjust as necessary. Clear soups, 3 percent vegetables, and salads are useful to complete vitamin and mineral requirements when the day's allotment of carbohydrate, protein, fat, and calories has been used.

TABLE 3. SAMPLE DAILY MEAL PLAN

Diet prescription
- 8 meat exchanges
- 3 fruit exchanges
- 3 milk exchanges
- 3 group A vegetable exchanges
- 2 bread exchanges
- 4 fat exchanges

Menus	Chores	Shopping list
	Breakfast	
Scrambled eggs	Thaw ground meat for dinner	1 dozen eggs
Bran muffins		1 box all-bran
Milk		1 quart fresh milk
Strawberries and cream		Strawberries
		Evaporated skim milk
	Lunch	
Crab salad	Make gelatin dessert, using strawberries from breakfast	Crab
Spinach soup		Spinach
Milk		Cantaloupe
Cantaloupe		
	Dinner	
Meat loaf		Ground meat
Green beans		Green beans
Cole slaw		Cabbage
Corn bread		Corn meal
Strawberry gelatin dessert		Sugar-free gelatin
Milk		

Step 5. Calculate the carbohydrate, protein, and fat content of each individual dish if you are dealing with a weighed diet, or of exchanges in the case of an exchange diet. If a permanent record is made of these calculations, they need be computed only once. Add each day's total of these components and adjust to fit the diet prescription. It will be necessary to rearrange meal plans, substituting a lower carbohydrate vegetable or adding extra protein to the main dish, in some cases. Check the distribution of food throughout the day and be certain that not more than one-third of the total daily allowance is taken at any one meal.

Step 6. Next to the meal plans, list each ingredient needed to prepare each dish. Take a separate sheet of paper and list those ingredients which you do not now have on hand. This comprises your next grocery shopping list. Consider the example in Table 3. If this method is followed, frequent trips to the grocery store are unnecessary, and considerable money is saved as the result. In addition, you always have what is needed to prepare each meal.

In practice, only Step 6 need be done more than once. Thus, considerable time is saved, not only shopping time but planning time as well. The diet prescription can be easily worked into the family meal plan, and you can be assured that nutritional needs are being met.

SPECIAL PROBLEMS

Some special problems must be taken into account when dealing with diabetic diets. Some of these are considered here and others are discussed in Chapter 10.

DELAYED MEALS

Diabetics who take insulin, and to a lesser degree, those who take the oral medications, must maintain a reasonably regular meal schedule. If this is altered to a significant degree, hypoglycemia results. Unfortunately, the evening meal is the one most often delayed, and this is also the time of day when hypoglycemia is most likely to occur. The danger is avoided most simply if the meal plan includes a nutritious beverage such as milk. Then, if the meal cooks slower than anticipated or if there is some interruption, the beverage can be taken by the diabetic member without disruption of the meal plan, and an insulin reaction can be averted. One should never wait, hoping that dinner will be ready before hypoglycemia occurs. Rather, hypoglycemia should be expected and avoided, since it is not only unpleasant but often harmful.

UNEXPECTED VISITORS

Not infrequently, people drop by unexpectedly and do not wish to stay for a meal. The diabetic may be embarrassed to interrupt the visit. Again, the problem can be avoided by including in each meal plan a glass of milk or other nutritious beverage that can be quickly taken by the diabetic member, avoiding both discomfort and physiologic unrest.

EATING IN RESTAURANTS

The most difficult thing to avoid in restaurant meals is extra fat. It is camouflaged in many ways and you can consume considerable quantities without realizing it. Remember that shellfish, fish, and fowl (in that order) contain the least amounts of inherent fat. Therefore, if extra fat is added in cooking, the total will be less than if you begin with a high-fat meal, such as beef or pork, and then add more. So, order seafood, preferably steamed, broiled, or poached. Request that salad dressings be served separately, so you can more carefully gauge the total amount than if it is already on the salad.

Carbohydrate is also generously served but is more easily recognized because of its bulk. If your carbohydrate allowance does not permit both bread and potato, request a substitute vegetable if potato is served. Most restaurants have beets and green beans available. Virtually all restaurants have a food scale available, and portions can be weighed if requested. If you know your diet well, this should not be necessary, however.

COCKTAIL PARTIES

These pose a triple threat—alcohol, snacks, and impaired judgment. Physicians are by no means in complete accord about permitting alcohol for diabetics. Those that permit it generally allow only hard liquor, such as whiskey, in very limited amounts, and forbid beer and wine. American beer usually contains about 4 percent carbohydrate, and if consumed, must be counted in the dietary calculations. Wine may contain a considerable amount of unfermented sugar and must not be taken. Whiskeys do not contain carbohydrate and are therefore often permitted. It is well to remember that the body cannot metabolize more than about 10 milliliters of alcohol per hour (that is about the quantity in an ounce of whiskey), and it is therefore not wise to drink

TABLE 4. CRACKER EXCHANGE VALUES

Type	Amount	Exchange value
Bacon Thins	15	1 bread, 2 fat
Blue cheese	12	1 bread, 1 fat
Cheese Tidbits	30	½ bread
Chippers, potato or bacon	8	1 bread, 1 fat
French Onion Thins	12	1 bread, 1 fat
Ritz	7	1 bread, 1 fat
Ry-Krisp	3	1 bread
Rye Thins	10	1 bread, 1 fat
Sesame Thins	10	1 bread, 2 fat
Three-ring pretzels	6	1 bread
Triangle thins	15	1 bread, 1 fat
Triscuit wafers	5	1 bread, 1 fat
Veri-Thin pretzel sticks	30	½ bread
Wheat Thins	12	1 bread

more than that amount. The alcohol in whiskey represents about 70 calories per ounce, and these calories must be counted, especially if weight control is a problem. A noncaloric mixer, such as plain water, soda, or plain quinine water, may be used freely. Some mixes contain sugar—so read the label.

Impaired judgment can be avoided if the rule of 1 ounce of whiskey per hour is adhered to strictly. A good way to do this is to order a tall, diluted drink and sip it slowly. This does not induce the alcoholic euphoria so widely desired, but it does prevent the hangover so abhorred.

Snacks can be taken in moderation, provided judgment is not impaired. Unfortunately, ordinarily reasonable alternatives in the forms of celery sticks, tomatoes, and carrot strips are completely offset by the high-fat mixtures they are either stuffed with or dipped into. It takes an extraordinary amount of self-control to eat a plain carrot strip when there is a bowl of cheese dip within reach. If it is your cocktail party, don't make the dip. If it is your friend's party, do your best with self-control. On the other hand, when the meal is delayed, snacks may actually be the means to avoid hypoglycemia, and if you suspect the meal may not be served on time, snack judiciously. Avoid snacks obviously high in carbohydrate and fat. These include dips of all kinds, cheese, sausages, and olives. Some pickles are quite sweet and must be avoided. Stick to the vegetables, if any; if none, small crackers in reasonable number can usually be compensated for at the evening meal (see Table 4 for exchange values of snack crackers).

CHAPTER 4

Food Preparation

There will be no attempt to teach basic cooking techniques in this book, since diabetics may prepare their food by all available methods. However, certain techniques will be mentioned which conserve or needlessly destroy nutrients. Vitamins and minerals are important because of the limited nature of the diabetic diet, and every effort should be made to conserve as many as possible.

Juices which escape during the preparation of meats and vegetables contain many vitamins and minerals and should be retained and used in some manner. Meat juices can be utilized in sauces, dips, and soups. They often contain B vitamins, as well as iron and other minerals. Ingenious cooks will have no problem disposing of these juices in a flavorful manner.

Many recipes call for soaking vegetables and suggest that the soaking water be discarded. If you have such a recipe in your files, discard it instead of the soaking water. All vegetables should have only a passing acquaintance with water prior to cooking. Except for leafy vegetables which may contain sand, most vegetables can be rinsed rapidly with cold water and cooked immediately. All B vitamins dissolve easily in water and can consequently be lost forever if either the soaking water or the cooking water is discarded. The cooking water (or pot liquid), especially of leafy green vegetables, makes a delightful clear soup. If you do not use the cooking water in this way, use it in sauces or as cooking liquid for other dishes; don't discard it.

COOKING METHODS

There are several methods of cooking vegetables that are unfamiliar to Americans, but have much to recommend them, with regard to both flavor and nutrition.

Butter-steaming requires the use of a heavy pot with a tight-fitting lid and a rack to hold the vegetables aloft. Coat the vegetables with as generous an amount of butter or margarine as your diet permits and place on the rack. Add ¼ cup of water in the bottom of the pan and cook at medium heat. Since there is almost no liquid, few nutrients are lost. The water should not be permitted to touch the vegetables.

Stir-frying, a method used by Oriental cooks, utilizes a heavy frying pan (or electric skillet) and a very small amount of cooking oil. The oil is heated quite hot, and the sliced vegetables are rapidly stirred while they are seared by the hot pan. The high heat carmelizes some of the starch in the vegetables and results in a surprisingly good flavor.

Waterless cooking can be accomplished with any heavy pan and a tight-fitting lid. This method uses the water already present in the vegetables by preventing its evaporation: They steam in their own juice. Regardless of the method used, the quicker cooking can be accomplished, the fewer nutrients are lost. Likewise smaller amounts of liquid are preferable to larger amounts, unless leftover liquid can be used to advantage.

Low-fat diets sometimes require special cooking techniques. The new, specially coated pans are good for sautéeing with little or no fat. These are marketed under a number of trade names, with Teflon being the most familiar. Well-seasoned cast-iron griddles can likewise be used. Both these utensils perform better if they are oiled and then wiped with a paper towel before and after using. This contributes a negligible amount of fat, but greatly increases their life and usability. Many foods can be cooked in the top of a double boiler with a smaller amount of fat than would be feasible in a skillet. For example, eggs can be scrambled without fat in the top of a double boiler. This is virtually impossible in a frying pan because of the higher heat and greater surface. Poaching is, of course, a good low-fat method of cooking eggs and meat. Unfortunately, the appearance is often unappetizing and consequently one is tempted to use a sauce to increase visual appeal. Use, instead, chives, parsley sprigs, grated citrus fruit peels, and similar condiments.

Marinating often enhances flavors. Unless specifically stated otherwise, we recommend the use of plastic bags for this phase of preparation. After all ingredients are added, remove all air and secure the top of the bag. This maneuver will cover all surfaces of the meat with a small amount of marinade. It is possible to turn the meat by kneading the closed bag. If all surfaces of meat are coated with marinade initially, it is not necessary to turn the meat again, as the marinade can not drain away in the airtight bag.

SEASONINGS

Diabetics need not concern themselves unduly about seasonings. All spices may be used as desired. Cooking wine may be used in moderation for special dishes, as these wines have little sugar. If a wine dish is simmered for at least one-half hour after the wine is added, the major part of the alcohol will evaporate. The carbohydrate, however, remains. Many physicians do not permit the use of cooking wine. It is my impression that an American housewife who uses wine in cooking more than once a month is most unusual. If you are one of those unusual American housewives and your physician has recommended a weighed diet, then some time must be spent adapting your recipes. Table 5 presents the carbohydrate content of wines commonly used in cooking. This, of course, must be figured into your diet calculations.

TABLE 5. CARBOHYDRATE CONTENT OF 1 OUNCE OF WINE

Wine	Carbohydrate (grams)	Alcohol (grams)	Calories
Brandy	0	10.5	73
Port	3.5	4.0	40
Sauterne	1.0	2.5	22
Sherry	2.4	4.5	30

Almost all commercial sauces contain some sugar. The amount is usually small, however, and diabetics can use these preparations, provided limited quantities are consumed.

SUGAR SUBSTITUTES

Although sugar must be avoided by diabetics, a number of other sweetening agents are available. These vary widely in sweetening ability and composition. It is best to rely upon the manufacturer's instructions when substituting in a recipe. Although these products are marketed under a variety of trade names, they contain one of the compounds listed below. Consult the label on your favorite product to see what the sweetening agent is.

Saccharin is the oldest of the noncaloric sweeteners. It has many times the sweetening power of sugar and must be used in small amounts. For many people saccharin has an unpleasant, bitter aftertaste, and when these people are also diabetic, it is unfortunate indeed. Saccharin is available in tablet and liquid form and can be used as directed on the package. It is not suitable for foods which must be cooked or frozen after the sweetener is added, as definite alteration of taste and loss of sweetness occur. It is most satisfactory when added immediately before serving.

Cyclamates offered a pleasant alternative to those who found saccharin unpalatable. Although there was no evidence that these compounds were harmful to human beings in amounts customarily used by diabetic patients, they have been ordered off the market by the Food and Drug Administration. This decision was based on animal experiments which suggested that large doses might be harmful.

Sorbitol is commonly found in the "dietetic" candies and gums. It is a carbohydrate and must be counted, both as carbohydrate and calories (4 calories per gram), in the diabetic diet. It causes little change in the blood sugar level and may be used in moderation by diabetics.

Lactose has only moderate sweetening ability and is sometimes combined with saccharin in commercial "artificial sugars." Like sorbitol, it can be used by diabetics, provided it is calculated as carbohydrate in the diet. These artificial sugars replace sugar on a volume-for-volume basis. This has obvious advantages to the cook who is trying to adapt a recipe, although such substitutions are not always successful. The artificial sugars have the disadvantage of being outrageously expensive and should be kept for special recipes. They are especially good for garnishing fresh fruits and give the appearance of powdered sugar. Some physicians object to the use of lactose because as it is broken down about half forms ordinary sugar. Ask your physician if you use significant amounts of these sweeteners. Table 6 presents sweetness equivalents.

TABLE 6. SWEETNESS EQUIVALENTS

Sugar	Sacch-arin (Saxin)	Sucaryl tablets	Sucaryl solution	Superose solution	Sweet-10 solution	Sweeta solution	Sweeta tablets	Artificial sugars*
1 tsp.	1	1	8 drops**	4 drops	1/8 tsp.	2 drops	1	1 tsp.
1 tbsp.	3	3	3/8 tsp.	12 drops	3/8 tsp.	6 drops	3	1 tbsp.
1/4 cup	12	12	1 1/2 tsp.	3/4 tsp.	1 1/2 tsp.	24 drops	12	1/4 cup
1/2 cup	24	24	1 tbsp	1 1/2 tsp.	1 tbsp.	1/4 tsp.	24	1/2 cup
1 cup	48	48	2 tbsp.	3 tsp.	2 tbsp.	1/2 tsp.	48	1 cup

* Sweetness and Light, Sugartwin, Sweet and Low.
** 8 drops = 1/8 tsp.

CHAPTER 5

Protein Foods

Although fish and other seafoods are included with meats in exchange lists, they have considerably less fat than beef, lamb, and pork, and should be used more frequently. A meat exchange is calculated to contain 7 grams of protein and 5 grams of fat. A meat exchange of shellfish contains 7 grams of protein but only 1 gram of fat, and consequently offers greater advantage than one would guess from looking at an exchange list. Of course, the merit of exchange lists is their simplicity: They offer average values rather than exact measures, and this accounts for the occasional discrepancy between the food content lists and the exchange lists presented in Chapter 1. For the patient with a very limited allowance of total fat or of saturated fat, the system of averages must be reevaluated with this in mind. The list below illustrates fat content in one meat exchange of common shellfish. Refer to Table 1 (Chapter 1) and note that while one exchange of meat is 1 ounce (30 grams), one exchange of shellfish is 1½ ounces (45 grams). Thus shellfish provides not only less fat but more food.

	C	P	F
Shrimps (raw)		8	0.4
Clams (raw)		6	0.7
Oysters (raw)	2	5	0.9
Scallops (raw)	2	7	0.1

These amounts of fat are sufficiently low to be disregarded unless large portions of fish are eaten. The usual serving of 3 ounces amounts to less than one-half fat exchange for all the shellfish listed above. Therefore, if fat intake is extremely limited, substitution of one serving of shellfish for one of beef permits use of additional fat in some other form. For example, if 3 ounces of scallops are substituted for 2 ounces of beef, 10 grams of fat (two fat exchanges) are "saved" for use in some other form—a significant saving indeed if your daily fat allowance is 50 grams or less. Because some forms of shellfish contain compounds known as sterols, which are similar to cholesterol, many physicians have been reluctant to include shellfish in low-fat diets. Current evidence indicates that ingestion of these fish does not raise blood fat levels, and this is the crucial point. I therefore feel they are permissible and even preferable to many other meats.

Many people have difficulty planning menus that provide adequate protein if the saturated fat allowance is very limited. If skim milk is not enjoyed, then a real crisis exists. Many seafood recipes are included in this chapter to encourage greater use of these foods. Most of them are relatively inexpensive and have little fat, and consequently fewer calories per pound than almost any other protein food. Americans would do well, nutritionally, to serve fish or other seafood daily. Weight watchers should be especially cognizant of the caloric advantages of these foods. Unfortunately, this advantage is often offset by the rich, fatty sauces with which these foods are deluged in most restaurants and many homes.

In addition to seafood, fowl such as turkey, chicken, pheasant, and quail can be used. However, like seafood, they must be prepared without added saturated fat. A variety of recipes are presented here which suggest suitable ways of preparing the low-fat meats. The final results are delicious and are sufficiently familiar in flavor and appearance so that families do not reject them.

The diabetic who must eat a low-fat diet is presented with a significant change in his eating habits. This diet can quickly become boring and intolerable unless the cook is imaginative.

Shellfish

CRAB MARINADE

	C	P	F
1 pound cooked crab meat	2	80	9
¼ cup oil			50
½ cup white wine vinegar	6		
½ cup dry white wine	5		
¾ teaspoon dry mustard			
1 clove garlic, crushed			
1 teaspoon salt			
⅛ teaspoon Tabasco sauce			
1 egg, beaten		7	5

Combine everything except egg and crab. Let flavors blend for about 30 minutes. Discard garlic. Add egg and mix until well blended. Add crab and pour mixture into a plastic bag. Refrigerate 1 hour. Remove meat from bag, drain off marinade, and serve the meat.

Each ounce (30 grams) contains 5 grams of protein, 1 gram of fat, and about 30 calories. A 3-ounce serving may be substituted for two meat exchanges. Only a negligible amount of marinade is retained by the crab and, therefore, it need not be counted.

CRAB PILAF

	C	P	F
1 pound cooked crab meat	2	79	9
1 tablespoon unsaturated margarine			11
1 medium onion, sliced	8	2	
1 can (10½ ounces) tomato soup	35	5	6
½ teaspoon salt			
¼ teaspoon pepper			
1 teaspoon dry mint			

Sauté the onion until clear. Add remaining ingredients and simmer 5 to 6 minutes. Serve with steamed rice. There should be about 3 cups total.

Measure total volume. One-fourth of total contains about 11 grams of carbohydrate, 22 grams of protein, 7 grams of fat, and approximately 200 calories. Each ½ cup of steamed rice contains 19 grams of carbohydrate and 2 grams of protein. A ½-cup serving of rice may be counted as one bread exchange; one-fourth of total crab mixture may be counted as three meat and one bread exchanges.

COMMENT. Serve this with a tossed green salad, without additional bread unless your carbohydrate allowance is generous. The dish can be prepared in advance by mixing all ingredients except the crab. The sauce actually improves with some age. It can be quickly heated and the crab added at the last minute for a quick meal. Since the crab has such low fat content, it may be necessary to include another fat exchange (5 grams) elsewhere in the meal. Although the protein content is equivalent to three meat exchanges, the fat content is not. This is very nice for those counting calories.

CRAB-STUFFED ONIONS

	C	P	F
4 large onions, shell only	10	2	
1½ cups cooked crab meat	3	44	6
¾ cup celery, minced	3	1	
¼ cup green pepper, minced	1		
¼ teaspoon curry powder			
1 tablespoon mayonnaise			11
⅛ teaspoon Tabasco sauce			

Parboil whole onions in salted water for about 10 to 15 minutes. Remove all inner layers and discard, leaving outermost one or two layers intact. Mix remaining ingredients and fill onions. Chill and serve.

One serving (one-fourth of total) contains 4 grams of carbohydrate, 12 grams of protein, 4 grams of fat, and about 100 calories. This amount may be substituted for two meat exchanges and one group A vegetable exchange.

COMMENT. If the onion is not eaten, delete the 4 grams of carbohydrate and 15 calories.

CRAB SALAD

	C	P	F
½ pound cooked crab meat	1	39	5
1 tablespoon lemon juice	1		
⅓ cup celery, finely chopped	1		
1 tablespoon green onion, finely chopped			
2 tablespoons green pepper, chopped	1		
½ teaspoon salt			
1 teaspoon mayonnaise			4
Several drops Tabasco sauce			
2 large tomatoes	15	2	

Slice tomatoes and arrange on four salad plates (or two plates if this is the main course). Mix mayonnaise, lemon juice, and Tabasco sauce together. Combine other ingredients. Add sauce and toss well. Place on top of tomato slices.

Entire recipe contains 19 grams of carbohydrate, 41 grams of protein, 10 grams of fat, and about 320 calories. Weigh or measure entire amount and divide by appropriate figure to obtain the amount in an individual serving.

The total volume is about 270 grams (9 ounces). If one-fourth is used for the diabetic portion, it will contain 5 grams of carbohydrate, 10 grams of protein, 2 grams of fat, and 80 calories. This may be counted as one group A vegetable and one and one-half meat exchanges.

GRILLED SHRIMP

2 pounds shrimp or prawns
1 package instant meat marinade
½ teaspoon basil
½ teaspoon tarragon
½ teaspoon celery seed

Dilute instant marinade according to directions on package and add herbs. Butterfly shrimp and dip into marinade. Barbecue immediately over coals or in oven. Baste with marinade as they cook. Should be done in about 5 minutes.

Each ounce contains 5 grams of protein, 1 gram of fat, and 30 calories. A 3-ounce serving may be substituted for two meat exchanges.

COMMENT. These can be quickly prepared. The marinade can be made any time and refrigerated. The shrimp can be swirled in the marinade and put in a strainer to drain while some are cooking. They make elegant party snacks or a tasty main dish served with rice or other vegetable and a salad.

SHRIMP WITH GREEN BEANS

	C	P	F
1 pound raw shrimp	7	82	4
2 pounds green beans, diagonally sliced	49	15	1
1 tablespoon oil			14
½ teaspoon salt			
⅛ teaspoon pepper			
¼ cup chicken bouillon		1	
1 tablespoon soy sauce	2		

Heat oil very hot in heavy pan; add beans and salt. Stir-fry about 4 minutes. Remove beans and stir-fry shrimp in same pan about 2 minutes. Add other ingredients, including beans. Cover and steam for 5 more minutes.

Each ounce of shrimp contains 5 grams of protein, 2 grams of fat, and 40 calories. A 3-ounce serving may be substituted for two meat exchanges. Up to 1 cup of beans equals one group A vegetable exchange.

COMMENT. Prawns may be substituted for shrimp without changing calculations.

SHRIMP IN TOMATOES

	C	P	F
1 pound cherry tomatoes	22	5	1
2 cans (4½ ounces each) broken shrimp	2	55	2
1 green onion	2		
1 tablespoon soy sauce	2		
3 black olives, chopped			4

Slice off stem ends of tomatoes and scoop out pulp. Chop shrimp into tiny pieces and combine with soy sauce, onion, and olives.

Fill tomato cavities. Serve as appetizers or on lettuce leaves as a salad.

Total recipe contains 27 grams of carbohydrate, 60 grams of protein, and 8 grams of fat. Divide by number of tomatoes to determine the approximate content of each.

SHRIMP AND WILD RICE

	C	P	F
1 tablespoon unsaturated margarine			11
1 onion, chopped	8	2	
1 pound fresh mushrooms	16	12	1
2 tablespoons lemon juice	2		
¼ cup chicken stock		1	
¼ cup dry white cooking wine	5		
½ teaspoon salt			
½ teaspoon tarragon			
½ teaspoon garlic salt			
1 pound shrimp	7	82	4
½ pound crab meat	1	39	4

Sauté onion in margarine; add mushrooms and lemon juice. Cook gently 2 to 3 minutes. Add shrimp and continue sautéeing until shrimp turn pink. Add remaining ingredients and simmer 2 to 3 minutes. Combine with cooked wild rice and let set for a few minutes until flavors have time to mix. Garnish with chopped tops of green onions or parsley. Serves six.

Each ⅓ cup of wild rice contains 15 grams of carbohydrate, 2 grams of protein, and 70 calories. This amount may be substituted for one bread exchange. Entire shrimp mixture contains 39 grams of carbohydrate, 136 grams of protein, and 20 grams of fat. One serving (one-sixth total shrimp mixture) contains 7 grams of carbohydrate, 23 grams of protein, 3 grams of fat, and 150 calories. This amount may be substituted for one group B vegetable and three meat exchanges. If fewer than six people are served, divide the totals above by the number of servings to calculate the content of each serving.

COMMENT. There are many pitfalls in calculating a mixed recipe such as the foregoing, and this has made those of us who work with diabetics leery of recommending mixed dishes or casseroles. When I say you can obtain the content of one serving by dividing the total content by the number of servings, I assume that the servings are equal. This is often not the case. If you are feeding small children or a mixed group, the servings may well differ in size. To calculate accurately, the portion to be measured must first be removed. Thus, if you are serving the foregoing recipe to three men and three women and wish to measure only one portion, you can proceed as follows:

1. Measure wild rice into small casserole or serving dish.
2. Measure total volume of shrimp mixture.
3. Remove one-sixth (or whatever fraction you wish) and add to wild rice in serving dish; cover and let flavors blend.
4. Serve remainder in usual way to the other diners.

PINKIE'S SHRIMP CREOLE

	C	P	F
1 large can (2½ cups) tomatoes	22	5	
2 medium onions, chopped	16	4	
1 medium green pepper, chopped	4		
2 teaspoons oil			10
1 clove garlic			
2 tablespoons flour	10	1	
2 bay leaves			
⅓ teaspoon celery seed			
¼ teaspoon thyme			
2 teaspoons parsley, minced			
2 tablespoons Worcestershire sauce			
1 pound cooked shrimp	7	82	4

Add onion, pepper, and garlic to oil in skillet and sauté 4 to 5 minutes. Blend in flour. Add tomatoes and seasoning. Simmer 30 minutes. Add shrimp and Worcestershire sauce and cook 15 minutes longer. Salt to taste. Serve on rice. Serves four.

Each ounce of shrimp contains 5 grams of protein and 1 gram of fat. A 3-ounce serving may be substituted for two meat exchanges. One-fourth of total amount of creole contains 15 grams of carbohydrate, 23 grams of protein, 4 grams of fat, and 190 calories. This amount may be substituted for one group B vegetable, one-half bread, and three meat exchanges.

CURRIED SHRIMP

	C	P	F
¼ cup unsaturated margarine			45
1 tablespoon curry powder			
1 medium onion	8	2	
2 tablespoons flour	12	2	
1¼ cups skim milk	15	10	
1 teaspoon salt			
⅛ teaspoon powdered ginger			
1 pound shrimp, shelled	7	82	4

Sauté shrimp in margarine until they change color; remove and keep warm. Add onion, ginger, and curry; cook until onion is clear. Add flour and stir until smooth. Add milk and stir until well mixed. Add salt and shrimp. Do not boil.

Each 1½ ounces (45 grams) of shrimp contains 7 grams of protein, 1 gram of fat, and 40 calories. This approximates one meat exchange. Total amount of sauce contains 35 grams of carbohydrate, 14 grams of protein, 45 grams of fat, and 600 calories. Apportion sauce equally and divide each of these figures by the number of servings to determine the content of one serving.

SCALLOPS ALMONDINE

	C	P	F
1 pound scallops	15	69	1
4 teaspoons margarine			15
¼ cup almonds, chopped	8	7	20
2 tablespoons lemon juice	2		
½ teaspoon salt			
Paprika			

Sprinkle scallops generously with paprika, then lemon juice. Melt margarine in metal baking dish and add almonds and scallops. Sprinkle salt over all. Bake in 350° oven for 15 minutes. The scallops will cook quickly. Serves four.

One serving (one-fourth total recipe) contains 6 grams of carbohydrate, 20 grams of protein, 9 grams of fat, and 185 calories. This may be substituted for three meat and one group A vegetable exchanges.

COMMENT. Unless all the sauce is eaten, the fat estimate given above is a little high. If you wish to take this into account, drain the scallops after cooking and measure the fat retrieved. The discarded fat can be subtracted from the total. This dish is good served with clam nectar, sliced tomatoes, and asparagus tips.

BAKED OYSTERS

1 pound oysters
Garlic salt
Black pepper
Onion flakes
Parmesan cheese

Leave oysters in half shell or put in individual serving dishes. Weigh or measure diabetic's portion before cooking. Sprinkle each serving with garlic salt, black pepper, onion flakes, and Parmesan cheese (not more than 1 teaspoon per serving). Bake in slow oven 30 minutes or until oysters curl around the edges.

Each 100 grams of raw oysters contains 6 grams of carbohydrate, 11 grams of protein and 2 grams fat. A 3-ounce serving approximates two meat exchanges and contains about 85 calories.

ABALONE SOUP

	C	P	F
½ pound abalone	8	42	1
2 cups chicken stock		8	
¼ pound fresh mushrooms	4	3	
Salt to taste			

Heat chicken stock to boiling; add mushrooms and abalone. Simmer 5 minutes. Serve with very thin lemon slices. Serves four as soup or two as a main course, accompanied by green salad and beverage.

Entire recipe contains 13 grams of carbohydrate, 53 grams of protein, negligible fat, and 270 calories.

COMMENT. Scallops may be substituted if abalone is not available in your area.

BROILED SCALLOPS

	C	P	F
1 pound scallops	15	69	1
⅓ cup skim milk	4	3	
1 teaspoon corn oil			5
¼ teaspoon paprika			
4 teaspoons lemon juice	1		

Use oil to grease pan. Toss scallops with lemon juice; then dip in milk. Placed in greased pan and sprinkle with paprika. Oven-broil until brown. Turn when necessary. Serves four.

Each 1½ ounces (45 grams) of scallops contains 7 grams of protein, 1 gram of fat, and about 35 to 40 calories. This amount may be substituted for one meat exchange.

Fish

TUNA AND VEGETABLES

	C	P	F
¼ cup oil or margarine			50
1 cup carrots thinly sliced	11	1	
1 cup green onions, diagonally sliced	11	1	1
1 cup celery, diagonally sliced	3		
2 cans (7 ounces each) water-packed tuna		112	3
1 can (5 ounces) bamboo sprouts	6	3	
¼ teaspoon salt			
½ cup dry sherry	9		
½ cup chicken bouillon		2	
1 cup spinach, shredded	3	2	
¼ cup soy sauce	6		

Heat oil in heavy pan; add carrots, onion, and celery and stir-fry for 3 to 4 minutes. Add tuna, bamboo sprouts, sherry, bouillon, and other seasonings. Simmer for 2 minutes and add spinach and soy sauce. Turn off heat, cover, and let set 2 to 3 minutes. Serve on steamed rice with pan sauce over the rice. Makes about 6 cups.

For weighed diets measure total. One serving (one-sixth total weight) contains 8 grams of carbohydrate, 20 grams of protein,

9 grams of fat, and 145 calories. One 1-cup serving counts as three meat exchanges and one group B vegetable exchange.

COMMENT. To adapt for low-fat diets, reduce amount of fat to 1 tablespoon. The entire recipe then contains 17 grams of fat and one serving contains 2 to 3 grams fat and about 130 calories.

TUNA PIE

	C	P	F
⅔ cup onion, chopped	10	1	
⅓ cup green pepper, chopped	1		
1 clove garlic, finely chopped			
1 large tomato, thinly sliced	9	2	1
2 tablespoons parsley, chopped			
1 teaspoon basil			
½ teaspoon salt			
⅛ teaspoon pepper			
2 cans (9¼ ounces each) water-packed tuna		147	5
pastry for two-crust pie (recipe follows)	86	43	102

Line pie pan with bottom crust. Combine onion, pepper, garlic, parsley, basil, and salt, and cover bottom of crust with about one-half the mixture. Add a layer of tuna and a layer of tomato slices. Repeat until all ingredients are used. Make at least two layers. Cover with remaining pie crust. Bake in 400° oven for 35 minutes. Cut pie into six equal servings.

Each slice contains 18 grams of carbohydrate, 32 grams of protein, 18 grams of fat, and 360 calories. This amount may be substituted for one bread, five meat, and one group A vegetable exchanges.

To adapt for a low-fat diet, omit the pie crust. Total recipe then contains 21 grams of carbohydrate, 150 grams of protein, and 4 grams of fat; a single serving contains 4 grams of carbohydrate, 24 grams of protein, 1 gram of fat, and 130 calories. This amount may be substituted for three meat and one group A vegetable exchanges.

COMMENT. It is not always possible to find water-packed tuna. If your grocer doesn't stock it, ask him to order some especially for you.

PIE CRUST

	C	P	F
¾ cup white flour	63	9	1
¾ cup soy flour	22	27	9
⅛ teaspoon salt			
½ cup unsaturated margarine, frozen			92
2 egg whites, unbeaten		6	

Using a fork, blend margarine, salt, and flour until the crumbles are about the size of small peas. Add egg whites and hand-mold mixture into halves. Roll out on a lightly floured board and fit bottom crust to pan.

TUNA SALAD

	C	P	F
1 cup carrots, shredded	10	1	
1 cup zucchini, shredded	6	2	
1 can (7 ounces) water-packed tuna		56	2
1 tablespoon pickle, chopped	4		
1 teaspoon celery seed			
1 tablespoon lemon juice	1		
Shredded lettuce			
2 tomatoes, cut in wedges	14	3	
⅓ cup toasted sliced almonds	10	9	27
⅓ cup low-calorie mayonnaise	8	6	2

Reserve tomatoes, almonds, and lettuce. Mix other ingredients until well blended. Arrange salad on beds of shredded lettuce; add tomato wedges and garnish with toasted almonds. Serves six.

The entire recipe contains 53 grams of carbohydrate, 77 grams of protein, 31 grams of fat, and vitamins A, B, and C. A ⅔-cup serving contains 9 grams of carbohydrate, 13 grams of protein, 5 grams of fat, and 135 calories. This amount may be substituted for one group B vegetable and two meat exchanges.

COMMENT. Serve with a hearty vegetable soup and milk to make a complete meal. A weight watcher might combine with a clear soup and skim milk for a nutritious and relatively low-calorie meal.

exchange. Total volume of sauce is about 6 cups. One serving (one-sixth total amount) contains 15 grams of carbohydrate and equals one bread exchange.

COMMENT. Any combination of shellfish and fish can be used in this dish. The flavor is improved if the shells are left on during cooking, but this does not add to the ease of eating. Shells may complicate the weighing process if the meat must be weighed.

SMOTHERED FISH

	C	P	F
2 pounds fish, white	1	180	10
4 mushrooms, chopped	2	1	
1 tablespoon ginger root, sliced	1		
1 teaspoon chicken stock concentrate	1	1	
1 green onion	2		
2 tablespoons soy sauce	3		
Few drops of oil			

Oil bottom of glass baking dish and place fish on bottom. Sprinkle chicken concentrate over fish; add sliced ginger root, chopped mushrooms, green onion, and soy sauce. Cover and bake in slow oven (about 250°) for 15 to 20 minutes. Serves approximately 6.

Each ounce of fish contains 7 grams of protein, 2 grams of fat, and about 50 calories. This amount equals one meat exchange. The carbohydrate content is negligible and need not be counted.

CREOLE-STYLE HALIBUT

	C	P	F
2 pounds fresh halibut		175	10
1 tablespoon onion, minced	1		
½ green pepper, minced	3		
¼ teaspoon pepper			
1 bay leaf, crumbled			
2 cups canned tomatoes	16	4	

Simmer ingredients in skillet for approximately 15 to 20 minutes. Makes six servings.

One serving (one-sixth of total) contains 3 grams of carbohydrate, 29 grams of protein, 3 grams of fat, and 155 calories. This amount may be substituted for four meat and one group A vegetable exchanges.

COMMENT. Any white fish may be substituted for halibut in this recipe.

SMOKE-FLAVORED HALIBUT

	C	P	F
2 pounds halibut steaks		190	11
1/3 cup soy sauce	8		
2 tablespoons sherry	3		
1/2 teaspoon smoke flavoring			
1/2 teaspoon grated ginger root			
1 tablespoon hoisin sauce			

Combine all ingredients in a plastic bag and marinate 1 hour or longer in refrigerator. Remove fish from plastic bag to covered dish, discard marinade, and bake fish in 250° oven for 20 minutes or until it flakes easily. Serve with leafy green vegetable and corn bread.

Each ounce of fish contains 7 grams of protein, 2 grams of fat, and 50 calories. This is one meat exchange.

SALMON STEAKS WITH DRESSING

	C	P	F
Salmon steaks			
1 small onion, chopped	6	1	
1/4 cup unsaturated margarine			45
1 cup bread crumbs	45	6	
1/2 teaspoon salt			
1/4 teaspoon allspice			
1/4 teaspoon pepper			
1/4 cup grapefruit juice	6		

Coat bottom of baking dish with small amount of margarine. Place steaks on bottom of baking dish. Sauté onion in remainder of margarine and add bread crumbs, salt, allspice, and pepper. Pour grapefruit juice over steaks and put bread-crumb mixture around. Garnish with grapefruit sections. Bake in 350° oven for 10 minutes or until dressing is fairly dry and fish flakes easily.

Each ounce of salmon contains 7 grams of protein, 2 grams of fat, and about 50 calories. Total amount of dressing contains 57 grams of carbohydrate, 7 grams of protein, and 45 grams of fat. One serving (¼ cup of dressing) contains 13 grams of carbohydrate, 2 grams of protein, and 11 grams fat. This amount of dressing equals one bread and two fat exchanges.

COMMENT. This dish is another example of the advantages of calculating exchanges on the basis of weight. A 3-ounce serving of salmon steak contains 21 grams of protein and 6 grams of fat. Because of the protein content, the exchange list counts this as three meat exchanges and assumes 15 grams of fat as part of the meat. However, the low fat content of the salmon permits the dressing to be added to the fish, for the following count:

	C	P	F
¼ cup dressing	13	2	11
3 ounces salmon		21	6
Total	13	23	17

The combination then equals one bread exchange (15 grams of carbohydrate, 2 grams of protein) and three meat exchanges (21 grams of protein, 15 grams of fat).

Obviously, the more clearly you understand weights, the better you can cope with a diet, whether exchange or weighed. I urge you to learn the content of foods commonly used in your diet so that greater versatility will be possible.

GRILLED SALMON

Salmon steaks, 1-inch thick
¼ teaspoon garlic salt
1 teaspoon lime juice
¼ cup soy sauce

Mix garlic salt, lime juice, and soy sauce, and marinate steaks in mixture for 1 hour. Drain off marinade and broil steaks about

10 minutes on each side. If oven broiler is used, place broiler in lowest position.

Weigh each portion of steak. Each ounce (30 grams) contains 7 grams of protein, 2 grams of fat, and about 50 calories. This equals one meat exchange. A 3-ounce serving contains 21 grams of protein, 6 grams of fat, and 150 calories. This amount equals three meat exchanges.

COMMENT. If fresh salmon steaks are not available in your area, try swordfish. Swordfish is somewhat drier but still quite tasty. The calculations are interchangeable. Salmon just happened to be plentiful when the recipe was tested.

SMOKED SALMON STEAKS

Salmon steaks
¼ cup soy sauce
2 tablespoon sherry or 1 tablespoon lime juice
½ teaspoon smoke flavoring
½ teaspoon grated ginger root or ¼ teaspoon powdered ginger
1 tablespoon hoisin sauce

Combine all ingredients except salmon steaks. Marinate steaks in mixture for at least 1 hour. Remove from marinade, place on rack and bake in 325° oven for 20 to 30 minutes or until fish flakes easily.

Each ounce of salmon contains 7 grams of protein, 2 grams of fat, and approximately 50 calories.

COMMENT. The ginger root and hoisin sauce can be purchased in Oriental markets or in the specialty food sections of many large supermarkets. Powdered ginger is not nearly so flavorful as the grated ginger root, but is better than no ginger at all. There is no substitute for the hoisin sauce. This is usually sold in a small tin. Remove the total contents after opening and store in a tightly covered refrigerator jar. It will keep for several months. Hoisin sauce is composed of soybeans, brown beans; and spices. Some brands also list sugar as an ingredient. Since the sauce is always used in small quantities as a marinade, this need not be included in calculations.

Fowl

SMOKED TURKEY ROAST

2½ pounds boneless turkey roast
2 tablespoons liquid smoke
1 teaspoon dried thyme
⅛ teaspoon cayenne
1 tablespoon lemon juice

Mix all ingredients in a plastic bag large enough to hold turkey roast. Wrap bag around roast and remove all the air. All surfaces of roast should be covered with marinade. Put in refrigerator and leave overnight or for several hours. Remove plastic bag and bake turkey according to directions on the package.

Each ounce contains 7 grams of protein, 3 grams of fat, and 50 calories. This amount may be substituted for one meat exchange.

CHICKEN BREASTS WITH ORANGE SAUCE

	C	P	F
1½ pounds chicken breasts, deboned		140	16
1 teaspoon salt			
½ teaspoon paprika			
¼ cup unsaturated margarine			45
1 tablespoon orange rind, grated	2		
1 cup orange juice	26	2	
1 teaspoon dried tarragon			
1 orange, sliced	18	2	

Sprinkle chicken breasts with salt and paprika; brown lightly in margarine. Add orange juice, rind, and tarragon. Cook in slow oven for 30 minutes. When done remove chicken and cook sauce over high heat to reduce volume. Serve sauce over chicken and/or steamed rice. Garnish with orange slices.

Measure total amount of sauce. One-fourth of entire amount contains 12 grams of carbohydrate, no protein, and 11 grams of fat. Each ounce of chicken contains about 7 grams of protein and 3 grams of fat. A 3-ounce serving of chicken and one-fourth of the total amount of sauce equal one bread and three meat exchanges.

COMMENT. This dish requires a very simple salad—almost any kind of dressing competes with the piquant flavor of the sauce. Plain lettuce sprinkled with paprika combines better than anything we tried.

CHICKEN LITTLE

	C	P	F
1 broiling or frying chicken, cut in service pieces			
1 tablespoon oil			14
1 teaspoon salt			
1/8 teaspoon pepper			
1/2 teaspoon paprika			
Juice of one-half lemon	2		
1/2 cup water			
1/4 teaspoon dried savory			
1/4 teaspoon dried thyme			
1 clove garlic (optional)			
1 medium onion, sliced	8	2	
1 medium green pepper, cut in strips	3	1	
1/4 pound mushrooms (optional)	4	3	

Sprinkle chicken with salt, pepper, and paprika. Brown in skillet in 1 tablespoon oil for 20 minutes, starting with skin side down. Add lemon juice, water, herbs, and garlic. Cover and cook 10 minutes. Add vegetables, cover and cook 10 minutes longer, or until chicken is tender.

Each ounce of chicken contains 7 grams of protein, 3 grams of fat, and approximately 50 calories. One-fourth of the vegetables (including mushrooms) contains 4 grams of carbohydrate, 2 grams of protein, and 25 calories. This amount of vegetables may be substituted for one group A vegetable exchange.

COMMENT. Remove the bones of the chicken before weighing. A thigh or drumstick of a 3-pound chicken will usually contain about 1 1/2 ounces of meat.

EAST INDIAN CHICKEN

3 pounds chicken, cut up or quartered
1 cup low-fat yogurt or buttermilk
1 clove garlic, crushed
½ teaspoon ground ginger
½ teaspoon ground cloves
½ teaspoon ground cinnamon
1 teaspoon salt
2 bay leaves

Mix all ingredients and marinate overnight or several hours at least. Remove chicken from yogurt mixture and barbecue over grill or in oven until tender. Serves about four.

Each ounce of meat contains 7 grams of protein, 3 grams of fat, and 50 calories. This amount may be substituted for one meat exchange.

COMMENT. Estimate the meat at 1½ ounces per thigh, drumstick or ½ breast. The appearance is completely ruined by removing the bones.

MINT CHICKEN

3 to 4 pounds chicken, skinned and boned
¼ teaspoon pepper
1 teaspoon oil
1 medium onion, chopped
1 teaspoon curry powder
2 tablespoons chopped fresh mint or
  1 tablespoon dried mint
1 tablespoon thinly sliced fresh ginger root or
  1 teaspoon ground ginger
1 tablespoon lime juice
2 teaspoons salt

Sprinkle chicken with salt and pepper and set aside. Sauté onions in oil and add curry; stir until onions change color. Add other ingredients, plus ¼ cup water, and simmer until well blended. Add chicken, cover and simmer about 45 minutes. Serve with rice, using all broth over the rice.

Each ounce of meat contains 7 grams of protein, 3 grams of fat, and about 50 calories. This amount may be substituted for one meat exchange. Carbohydrate content is negligible.

SMOKED CHICKEN

3 to 4 pounds chicken, skinned
1/3 cup soy sauce
2 tablespoons cooking sherry (or 2 tablespoons chicken broth and 1/4 teaspoon vinegar)
1/2 teaspoon smoke flavoring
1/2 teaspoon grated ginger root (or 1/8 teaspoon powdered ginger)
1 teaspoon salt
1 tablespoon hoisin sauce

Combine all ingredients in a plastic bag. Marinate for 3 to 4 hours or overnight. Remove chicken from bag, drain off marinade, and bake chicken at 325° for 1½ hours. Can be served hot or cold.

Each ounce of meat contains 7 grams of protein, 3 grams of fat, and about 50 calories. This amount may be substituted for one meat exchange.

This marinade is also good when used on turkey or any mild-flavored fowl.

COMMENT. Remove the bone from the portion to be weighed before cooking, or estimate 1½ ounces of meat per drumstick, thigh, or ½ breast.

OVEN-FRIED CHICKEN

1 frying chicken
4 tablespoons cornflake crumbs
Seasoning salt

Skin chicken and sprinkle generously with seasoning salt. Shake in a paper bag with cornflake crumbs. Bake in lightly greased baking pan, uncovered, at 375° for 45 minutes. Leave ample space between pieces and turn once during baking.

Each ounce contains 7 grams of protein, 3 grams of fat, and 50 calories. One ounce may be substituted for one meat exchange.

COMMENT. Either remove the chicken bones before weighing or estimate at 1½ ounces meat for one thigh or drumstick, or ½ breast.

HANNAH SPIELHOLZ'S CHICKEN

	C	P	F
3 pounds chicken, deboned			
2 large cloves garlic, chopped			
1 teaspoon dried rosemary			
1 scant teaspoon poultry seasoning			
3 ounces dry sherry	7		
1½ tablespoons oil			21
1 can (4 ounces) button mushrooms	2	2	
1 can (8 ounces) tomato purée	20	4	
1 can (4 ounces) black olives	2	1	14
Salt and pepper to taste			

Heat oil in heavy pan and brown chicken on all sides. Sprinkle with salt and pepper. Add garlic, poultry seasoning, and rosemary. Cover and let simmer 10 minutes. Add mushrooms, olives, and tomato purée. Cover and cook over low heat until tomato sauce thickens (about 45 minutes), stirring frequently. Increase heat and add wine. Cook 5 minutes more, basting frequently. Serve with rice. Serves six to eight.

Each ounce of chicken contains 7 grams of protein, 3 grams of fat, and approximately 50 calories. Each black olive contains about 1 gram of fat and 10 calories. If the sauce is served over the rice, measure the total volume of sauce and divide by the number of servings to get the amount of one serving. For example, a total of 3 cups of sauce contains 31 grams of carbohydrate and 35 grams of fat. One serving (½ cup, or one-sixth total volume) contains 5 grams of carbohydrate and 6 grams of fat.

In this case the carbohydrate content is low and can be disregarded by most patients; however, 6 grams of fat is significant and should be considered in any diet. The 6 grams of fat may be substituted for one fat exchange.

CHICKEN AND PEANUT SOUP

	C	P	F
1 stewing hen, skinned			
1 cup (150 grams) raw shelled peanuts	24	39	73
3 quarts water			
4 teaspoons salt			
2 green onions, whole			
2 tablespoons cooking sherry	1		
1 teaspoon sliced ginger root or ¼ teaspoon powdered ginger			

Soak peanuts in boiling water for 20 to 30 minutes. Place chicken in large covered pan and add all ingredients except peanuts. Simmer 2 hours. Add peanuts with soaking liquid and simmer another 2 hours. Discard onions. Remove any obvious fat. Cut chicken in cubes and serve in bowls with broth.

Each serving of 1 cup of broth, 1 ounce of cubed chicken, and 1 ounce (2 tablespoons) of peanuts contains 5 grams of carbohydrate, 20 grams of protein, 17 grams of fat, and 250 calories. This amount approximates three meat exchanges and one group A vegetable exchange.

COMMENT. This is an unusual, tasty dish. It is quite filling and can be served with a cottage cheese and fruit salad for a light meal. Raw peanuts are often hard to find and outside the Southeast may seldom be available. The small red Spanish variety is sometimes packaged and sold along with dried beans in other parts of the country.

ANGELA'S PHEASANT

	C	P	F
½ pound pheasant, deboned		56	24
1 large green pepper	3	1	
1 large tomato	8	2	
½ pound fresh mushrooms	8	6	
½ cup pecans	6	5	37
1 teaspoon oil			5
2 tablespoons soy sauce	3		
½ teaspoon hoisin sauce			

Heat oil very hot in heavy skillet. Dice all ingredients and arrange on platter near stove. Add pheasant to skillet first and stir-fry until brown on all sides. Remove to warm platter. Add mushrooms and stir-fry for 1 to 2 minutes; then add pepper, tomato, and cooked pheasant. Turn off heat. Place a bed of steamed rice on serving plates. Put pheasant and vegetables on rice, weighing or measuring as necessary. Add soy and hoisin sauces to skillet and heat to simmering. Drizzle over meat and vegetables. Garnish with pecan halves. Serves two as a full meal.

Each ounce of pheasant contains 7 grams of protein, 3 grams of fat, and about 50 calories. One-half the vegetables contains 10 grams of carbohydrate and may be substituted for one group B and one group A vegetable exchanges. Twelve pecan halves generously garnish one serving and add 10 grams of fat, 100 calories, and two fat exchanges.

COMMENT. This is a delicious and quick one-dish meal. Chicken can be substituted for the pheasant, but isn't as good.

Meat

EPICUREAN LAMB

(from the kitchen of Hanna W. Spielholz)

	C	P	F
2½ cups (500 grams) cooked lamb, cut in chunks		143	39
½ cup onions, chopped	7	2	
1 tablespoon corn oil			14
1 can (4 ounces) sliced mushrooms	2	2	
1 cup cooked rice (⅓ cup uncooked)	36	3	
1 can (2½ cups) tomatoes	20	5	
1 teaspoon salt			
⅛ teaspoon pepper			
½ teaspoon curry powder			
¼ cup Parmesan cheese		14	10

Cook onion in oil until golden. Add drained mushrooms and brown lightly. Combine all ingredients except cheese and place in greased 1½-quart casserole. Sprinkle with cheese and bake at 400° for 45 minutes, covered; uncover and bake 10 minutes. Serves six.

One serving contains 11 grams of carbohydrate, 28 grams of protein, 11 grams of fat, and 255 calories. This amount may be substituted for four meat, one-half bread, and one group A vegetable exchanges.

KATIE'S PERSIAN LAMB

(from the kitchen of Mrs. Thomas Ghavamian)

	C	P	F
2 medium eggplants	30	7	1
2 tablespoons oil			28
1½ pounds lamb (cut from leg into stew-meat pieces, all fat removed), cut 1-inch cubes		135	38
1 medium white onion, finely chopped	8	2	
1 teaspoon salt			
½ teaspoon cinnamon			
½ teaspoon pepper			
¼ teaspoon nutmeg			
3 dashes paprika			
6 tablespoons margarine			68
1 can (6 ounces) tomato paste	34	6	
2 cups water			
4 tablespoons lemon juice	4		
2 medium tomatoes, cut into wedges	12	3	

Cut unpeeled eggplants lengthwise into 1-inch slices. Wash and sprinkle with salt and let stand about 20 minutes to take out bitterness. Add oil to 4-quart saucepan or large skillet. Add meat, onions, and seasonings and sauté. Then add tomato paste, water, and lemon juice to meat and simmer over low fire for about 45 minutes to an hour, or until meat is tender. Wash salt off eggplants and dry. Add margarine to another skillet and sauté eggplants separately until browned and tender. About 15 minutes before meat is done, add cooked eggplants and tomato wedges to meat sauce and let cook very slowly (simmer) for these last 15 minutes. Serve with steamed rice or noodles. Serves six.

Measure or weigh entire recipe and take one-sixth of total for single portion. This portion contains 15 grams of carbohydrate, 26 grams of protein, 23 grams of fat, and 370 calories. This may be substituted for two group B vegetable and four meat exchanges.

COMMENT. Chicken may be substituted for the lamb.

LAMB AND SPRING ONIONS

	C	P	F
1½ pounds lean lamb, thinly sliced		135	35
¾ teaspoon Chinese Five Spice			
1 egg white		3	
2 cloves garlic, mashed			
6 slices fresh ginger	1		
2 tablespoons soy sauce	3		
6 tablespoons sherry	7		
2 tablespoons water			
10 green onions	19	2	
2 tablespoons corn oil			28

Marinate lamb in Five Spice, egg white, garlic, ginger, and soy sauce for 20 to 30 minutes using a plastic bag. Heat oil in heavy skillet until very hot; add lamb and stir until meat browns. Remove lamb and keep warm. Add marinade, sherry, water, and onions to skillet. Stir and simmer 3 to 5 minutes. Add meat and serve. Serves six.

One serving contains 5 grams of carbohydrate, 23 grams of protein, 11 grams of fat, and 210 calories. This amount may be substituted for three meat and one group A vegetable exchanges.

COMMENT. If necessary, ⅛ teaspoon powdered cinnamon, ⅛ teaspoon powdered cloves, and ¼ teaspoon aniseed can be used instead of Chinese Five Spice. The effect is not quite the same, but is acceptable.

GROUND BEEF WITH BUTTER BEANS

(from the kitchen of Mrs. Dorothy Rockwell)

	C	P	F
1 pound lean ground beef		94	45
1 medium onion, sliced	8	2	
1 green pepper, cut in strips	3	1	
1 can (15 ounces) butter beans (large limas)	57	17	1
Salt and pepper			

Brown ground beef. Add onion and green pepper. Cook only until pepper and onion are still crisp. Add butter beans *with liquid*, and heat. Add salt and pepper to taste. Serves four.

One serving contains 17 grams of carbohydrate, 28 grams of protein, 12 grams of fat, and 290 calories. This may be substituted for one bread and four meat exchanges.

BEEF SPINACH SCRAMBLE

	C	P	F
2 pounds very lean ground beef		188	91
2 tablespoons corn oil			28
1 medium onion, chopped	8	2	
1 clove garlic, mashed			
1¼ teaspoons nutmeg			
¼ teaspoon pepper			
¼ teaspoon oregano			
1 bunch (½ pound) spinach, chopped	8	7	
4 eggs		28	25
½ teaspoon salt			

Brown ground beef in oil. Add onions and garlic. Cook over low heat until onion is clear. Add seasoning and mix well. Stir in spinach. Cook over very low heat for 3 to 5 minutes. Add eggs and stir. Heat until eggs set. Serves about six.

One serving contains 3 grams of carbohydrate, 37 grams of protein, 24 grams of fat, and 375 calories. This may be substituted for five meat and one group A vegetable exchanges.

GINGER BEEF WITH LITTLE GREEN ONIONS

	C	P	F
1½ pounds lean beef, thinly sliced		147	32
1 clove garlic, mashed			
8 slices fresh ginger	1		
2 tablespoons soy sauce	3		
3 tablespoons cooking sherry	4		
3 tablespoons water			
12 small green onions	21	2	
2 tablespoons corn oil			28

Marinate beef in garlic, 1 tablespoon soy sauce, and ginger for 30 minutes. Chop green onions into 1-inch pieces. Heat oil in a heavy pan and add onions. Cook until limp. Remove onion, add beef mixture, and cook until beef browns slightly. Add sherry, water, and remaining soy sauce. Heat to serving temperature. Serves four.

One serving contains 7 grams of carbohydrate, 37 grams of protein, 15 grams of fat, and 310 calories. This may be substituted for five meat and one group B vegetable exchanges.

BEEF WITH BROCCOLI

(from the kitchen of Mrs. Thomas Chinn)

	C	P	F
½ pound lean beef, sliced thin		49	10
1 pound broccoli	16	10	
2 tablespoons soy sauce	3		
1 tablespoon sherry	1		
1 tablespoon cornstarch	7		
½ teaspoon salt			
1 tablespoon sesame oil			14
1 tablespoon corn oil			14
2 tablespoons water			

Cut broccoli spears, then slit into two to four sections. Slice stalk into thin slices. Mix cornstarch, soy sauce, sesame oil, sherry, and beef. Heat ½ tablespoon corn oil in frying pan until hot. Stir-fry broccoli and salt for 1 minute. Add 2 tablespoons water and cook for 2 more minutes; remove from pan and set aside. Again, heat ½ tablespoon corn oil in frying pan until hot. Stir-fry beef mixture for 2 minutes. Add broccoli to beef mixture and stir well for 2 minutes. Serve hot. Serves three.

One serving contains 9 grams of carbohydrate, 20 grams of protein, 13 grams of fat, and 230 calories. This may be substituted for three meat and one group B vegetable exchanges.

COMMENT. Fresh asparagus can be substituted for broccoli. Calculations remain the same.

BEEF WINE STEW

(from the kitchen of Hanna W. Spielholz)

	C	P	F
2 pounds lean stewing beef, cubed		193	67
1 tablespoon corn oil			14
Salt and pepper			
2 cloves garlic			
1 cup tomato purée	22	4	
½ cup dry red wine	4		
2 onions, thinly sliced	17	3	
2 large carrots, thinly sliced	19	2	
Large pinch of thyme			

Brown beef thoroughly in corn oil in heavy pan. Season well with salt and pepper (approximately 1 teaspoon salt, ¼ teaspoon pepper). Add chopped garlic, thyme, tomato purée, and wine; cover and simmer for 1 hour or 15 minutes in pressure cooker. (If cooked under pressure, reduce heat rapidly under cold running water.) Add onions and carrots and *simmer* gently until tender (45 minutes). Add salt and pepper to taste. Serve with rice. Serves six.

One serving contains 10 grams of carbohydrate, 34 grams of protein, 14 grams of fat, and 300 calories. This may be substituted for five meat and one group B vegetable exchanges.

TOMATO MEAT LOAF

(from the kitchen of Mrs. Dorothy Rockwell)

	C	P	F
2 pounds ground meat		162	90
1 can (7½ ounces) tomato sauce, unsweetened	20	4	6
⅓ cup saltines (8 crushed)	20	3	3
¾ cup onion, chopped	10	2	
½ cup fresh parsley, chopped (or ¼ cup dried)	6	3	
1 egg		7	6
1 tablespoon Worcestershire sauce	3		
½ teaspoon dry mustard			
½ teaspoon salt			
¼ teaspoon pepper			

Combine ¾ cup tomato sauce with other ingredients. Meat loaf should be baked on a broiler pan so fat can drain off. Cover with aluminum foil tent to retain moisture. Bake in 375° oven approximately 1¼ hours. During last 5 minutes remove aluminum foil and spoon remaining ¼ cup tomato sauce over meat loaf. Do not overcook or meat will be dry. Serves 8.

Each serving contains 7 grams of carbohydrate, 23 grams of protein, 13 grams of fat, and 235 calories. This may be substituted for one-half bread and three meat exchanges.

COMMENT. To approximate eight equal servings, mound meat loaf in a half-moon shape and cut into eight equal pie-shaped pieces.

SPICED PORK AND VEAL

(from the kitchen of Mrs. Thomas Chinn)

	C	P	F
1 pound lean ground pork		89	41
½ pound lean ground veal		44	22
½ teaspoon pepper			
½ teaspoon salt			
⅛ teaspoon nutmeg			
⅛ teaspoon mace			
¼ teaspoon sage			
2 tablespoons bread crumbs	8	1	
2 tablespoons water			

Mix ingredients well and shape into patties. Cook in a nonsticking pan until well browned. Add water, cover, and simmer 10 minutes. Serve pan juices along with meat. The portion for the diabetic can be measured before or after cooking. Serves about six.

One serving contains negligible carbohydrate, 22 grams of protein, 11 grams of fat, and 185 calories. This may be substituted for three meat exchanges.

BARBECUED PORK
(from the kitchen of Mrs. Thomas Chinn)

	C	P	F
1/4 cup soy sauce	6		
2 tablespoons salad oil			28
1/8 teaspoon cayenne pepper			
1/8 teaspoon ground cinnamon			
1/8 teaspoon ground cloves			
1 pound lean pork roast (fat trimmed off) or 3 pounds lean ribs		87	46

Cut pork into bite-size pieces. Combine ingredients in plastic bag and marinate 1 to 2 hours. Remove meat from bag and discard marinade. Put meat on small rack or skewers and bake at 325° for 1 hour.

Each ounce (30 grams) of cooked pork contains 7 grams of protein, 5 grams of fat, and 75 calories. This can be substituted for one meat exchange.

Soybeans

ROASTED SOYBEANS

	C	P	F
1 cup dry soybeans	57	68	35
1 can (3 ounces) bamboo shoots	4	2	
1/2 cup soy sauce	12		
2 tablespoons molasses	27		
1/4 teaspoon aniseeds			
2 quarts water			

Place beans and 2 cups water in a pan and freeze. When ready to cook remove from freezer and add remaining water. Heat to boiling. Reduce heat and simmer about 1 hour or until tender. Beans can be cooked without prior freezing but it takes much longer. Add more water as necessary. When beans are tender, add other ingredients and bake at 350° for about 1 hour. Beans should be coated with sauce, but no liquid should remain in the pan. Serves six.

One serving contains 17 grams of carbohydrate, 12 grams of protein, 6 grams of fat, and 170 calories. This may be substituted for one bread and two meat exchanges.

COMMENT. Soybeans make a satisfactory meat substitute. Although they are relatively high in carbohydrate content, this is tempered by the amount of protein and fat they also contain. The fat is, of course, mostly unsaturated.

Eggs

Some of the following recipes utilize only the whites of eggs in order to eliminate the saturated fat contained in egg yolks. If you are permitted saturated fat, whole eggs can be used in any of the recipes, and the yellow coloring omitted. Remember that 5 grams of fat, 3 grams of protein, and 60 calories are present in an average egg yolk, and these amounts must be added for *each* egg yolk added. Numerous nutrients are added as well.

EGGS WITH SCALLOPS

	C	P	F
1 pound scallops	15	70	1
6 egg whites	2	20	
3 tablespoons leek, finely chopped	3		
2 tablespoons cooking oil			28
¼ teaspoon yellow food coloring			

Add scallops and leek to cooking oil. Sauté gently for 5 to 6 minutes or until the scallops are done. Beat egg whites and add yellow food coloring; pour over scallops. Stir until eggs are as done as you like. Serve immediately. Makes four generous servings.

Entire recipe contains 20 grams of carbohydrate, 90 grams of protein, and 30 grams of fat. One serving (one-fourth total amount) contains 5 grams of carbohydrate, 22 grams of protein, 7 grams of fat, and 170 calories. This equals three meat and one group A vegetable exchanges.

COMMENT. Shrimp may be substituted for the scallops. This dish is good for breakfast or brunch, or can be served with toasted English muffins, a green salad, and vegetable for a full meal.

EGG FLOWER SOUP

	C	P	F
6 cups chicken broth		24	
4 egg whites	1	14	
¼ teaspoon yellow food coloring			
¼ cup sliced mushrooms	2		
2½ teaspoons salt			
½ teaspoon sugar	3		

Beat egg whites with food coloring until well mixed but not too frothy. Bring broth and salt to boiling and add mushrooms. While broth is simmering, pour in egg mixture in a fine stream, stirring constantly. Set off heat and serve immediately. Makes about six cups.

Each cup contains about 6 grams of protein, negligible fat and carbohydrate, and 25 calories. This amount can be used for one meat exchange.

QUICHE LORRAINE

	C	P	F
¼ pound mushrooms	5	3	
1 tablespoon margarine			11
¼ teaspoon yellow food coloring			
6 egg whites, lightly beaten	2	20	
1½ cups evaporated skim milk	36	24	
6 ounces Swiss cheese, thinly sliced	3	50	50

Combine ingredients and pour into glass baking dish. Sprinkle top with nutmeg and bake in slow oven (325°) for 20 to 30 minutes or until consistency of custard. Serves six adequately as a main course.

One serving (one-sixth total pie) contains 8 grams of carbohydrate, 16 grams of protein, 10 grams of fat, and 186 calories. This equals two meat and one-half bread exchanges.

The quiche can be served with a green salad and low-calorie dressing.

COMMENT. I have altered the classic quiche recipe to decrease the amount of saturated fat and increase the unsaturated fat. It still contains some saturated fat, but the ratio of unsaturated to saturated is acceptable.

SCRAMBLED EGGS

	C	P	F
2 egg whites		7	
4 to 5 drops yellow food coloring			
2 tablespoons evaporated skim milk	3	2	
1/8 teaspoon salt			
1 tablespoon cooking oil or margarine			14

Heat oil in small pan. Beat remaining ingredients and add to hot oil. Stir briskly until properly set. Serves one.

Entire amount contains 3 grams of carbohydrate, 9 grams of protein, 14 grams of fat, and 174 calories. This may be substituted for one meat and two fat exchanges.

For low-fat diets, omit oil and cook in top of double boiler. This variation contains 3 grams of carbohydrate, 9 grams of protein, and 50 calories. If whole eggs are used, the product contains 3 grams of carbohydrate, 12 grams of protein, 24 grams of fat, and 275 calories.

FANCY SCRAMBLED EGGS

	C	P	F
6 whole eggs	2	42	36
4 tablespoons evaporated skim milk	6	4	
1 tablespoon soy sauce	2		
1 tablespoon bourbon			
2 tablespoons (20 grams) sesame seeds	3	4	10
2 tablespoons unsaturated margarine			23

Gently heat margarine in heavy skillet and add sesame seeds. Toast lightly. Beat eggs, bourbon, and milk. Add to sesame seeds and stir until properly set. Garnish each serving with 1 teaspoon soy sauce. Serves three or four.

Entire recipe contains 13 grams of carbohydrate, 50 grams of protein, and 69 grams of fat. One serving (approximately one-fourth total recipe) contains 3 grams of carbohydrate, 12 grams of protein, 17 grams of fat, and 210 calories. This is equivalent to two meat and one fat exchanges.

For low-fat diets, reduce margarine to 1 tablespoon and sesame seeds to 1 tablespoon. Omit egg yolks and include ¼ teaspoon yellow food coloring. In this case, the entire dish contains 12 grams of carbohydrate, 26 grams of protein, and 16 grams of fat.

CHAPTER 6

Carbohydrate Foods

Most diabetics are severely limited in the amount of carbohydrate they may eat. Although this amount varies within wide limits, depending upon amount of exercise taken, age, weight, and numerous other factors, it is seldom greater than 200 grams per day. Further, this carbohydrate must be taken in a long-acting form. As discussed earlier, the simple sugars cause the blood sugar level to rise much higher than do starch and other complex carbohydrates. Likewise, the combination of simple sugars with protein and fat causes some delay in their absorption and decreases the amount of rise in the blood sugar. These recipes, therefore, include as much protein and fat as is practical without altering the flavor of the final results. In most cases, this results in an increase in calories but it also gives more nutrition and less carbohydrate for each serving. Rich desserts are not for serious weight watchers in any case, and many diabetics must be serious weight watchers.

Dessert cookery presents the greatest challenge and usually the greatest disappointment to the fledgling diabetic cook. Our tastes are accustomed to foods sweetened with sucrose (table sugar), and nothing else quite matches the taste. All the many nonsugar sweeteners available commercially can be used to sweeten various foods. None reproduces the taste of sucrose, however. Many problems appear as soon as sugar is eliminated from a recipe. When a few spoonfuls of liquid are substituted for a cup or two of sugar, disastrous things happen to the texture of many desserts. At least two sweeteners are available in powdered form that can be substituted for sugar in identical volume. Both contain lactose, however, and the carbohydrate must be counted in the diet calculations. A limited amount of these sweeteners can be used by diabetics. They are both quite expensive. If the saccharin compounds are cooked or frozen, an unpleasant flavor results and the sweetness diminishes. Finally, one must acknowledge that only sugar tastes like sugar. If the diabetic can accept once and for all this unpleasant truth and cease the search for a sweetener that reproduces the exact taste of sugar, he may actually come to appreciate these marvelous chemicals that taste sweet, yet carry no (or few) calories and cause no tooth decay or wild fluctuations of blood sugar level. When using these sweeteners it is wise to recognize what they will not do, as well as what they will do. In my experience they will not work well in baking cakes. Numerous cake recipes using unsaturated fat and artificial sweeteners have been tried, but without exception the cakes have been heavy and unpalatable compared with cakes made in the usual way. Accordingly, these cake recipes have been omitted. There is a recipe for a Christmas cake that uses a very small amount of sucrose and could be justified for such a special occasion. The problem of birthday cakes for small children is undoubtedly a significant one, but I have not found the solution.

Ice creams constitute another source of disappointment. Many variations have been tried, but were not worth the effort involved in making them.

In contrast to cakes, delicious pies can be made using the artificial sweeteners, and if your diet permits unlimited calories and fat, by all means do some experimenting of your own.

Fruit-based desserts provide the best medium for the artificial sweeteners and many commonly available fruits are used in the desserts described. They are all nutritious, delicious, and simple to prepare. Most are adaptable to fruits other than those recommended in the recipes, so try whatever you have available locally. In general, the calculations will need little alteration.

Bread, Cookies, and Cakes

SOURDOUGH BREADS

Sourdough is the simplest of the yeast breads and is especially useful for low-saturated-fat diets. These breads require the use of sourdough starter (recipe follows), which can be perpetuated indefinitely by a determined housewife. It is customary among sourdough fanciers to give a portion of the starter to friends and neighbors. This friendly gesture is a form of enlightened self-interest. If your starter "goes bad" and you've shared it with many friends, your chances of having the favor returned are much better. A good starter improves with age and should be used or freshened at least once weekly. If properly cared for it will last for years.

SOURDOUGH STARTER

	C	P	F
3 cups white flour	250	35	3
2 cups skim milk	24	16	
1 package yeast	1	1	
¼ cup warm water			

Combine yeast and warm water. When dissolved, add to milk and flour. Stir until smooth. Put in a covered glass or plastic container at least 1 quart in volume. Let rise in refrigerator for several days. When dough is quite spongy and has a pleasant sourdough odor, it is ready to use. Never use all the starter. Always keep 1 cup or more to perpetuate the process. If 1 cup of starter is used, replace with 1 cup of flour and ⅓ cup of skim milk. It can be used daily if replaced in this manner.

Each cup of starter contains 40 grams of carbohydrate, 8 grams of protein, and no fat. Total volume after rising is about 7 cups.

COMMENT. There are many ways to prepare sourdough starter. The best way is to get a portion from a friend. Occasionally these starters are available commercially and are found in specialty food stores, usually frozen. The above recipe is a compromise to be used when friends and commercial suppliers fail.

PINKIE'S SOURDOUGH HOT CAKES

(from the kitchen of Mary Pinckney Ferguson)

	C	P	F
½ cup starter	20	4	
2 cups warm water			
2 cups flour	167	26	2

Place starter in a medium-sized mixing bowl. Add warm water and flour. Beat well and set in a warm place, free from draft, to develop overnight. In the morning the batter will have gained one-half again its bulk and be covered with air bubbles. It will have a yeasty odor. Set aside ½ cup in a refrigerator jar as a starter for next time. To the remainder add:

	C	P	F
1 egg		7	6
1 tablespoon sugar	12		
1 teaspoon soda			
1 teaspoon salt			
2 tablespoons boiling water			
2 tablespoons oil			28

Dissolve dry ingredients in boiling water. Beat with a fork and blend in other ingredients. Bake on a hot griddle. Serves six.

Weigh or measure entire portion and take one-sixth of total for one serving. This amount contains 33 grams of carbohydrate, 6 grams of protein, 6 grams of fat, and 210 calories. This may be substituted for two bread and one fat exchanges.

QUICK SOURDOUGH MUFFINS

	C	P	F
½ cup white flour	42	6	
½ cup starter	20	4	
1 teaspoon baking powder			
½ teaspoon salt			

Combine flour, salt, and baking powder and mix well. Oil a 6-cup muffin tin. Mix starter and dry ingredients. Stir only until well mixed. Drop immediately into muffin tins. Keep volume of muffins about equal. Bake in preheated oven at 425° for 10 to

12 minutes or until well browned. Serve hot with unsaturated margarine.

Each muffin weighs about 30 grams and contains about 10 grams of carbohydrate, 2 grams of protein, and negligible fat. Measure margarine used for "buttering" and add 4 grams of fat and 36 calories for each teaspoon used. Three muffins may be substituted for two bread exchanges.

COMMENT. These muffins are quickly prepared and are good for breakfast. They are light and may be dressed with unsaturated margarine at the table.

CORN BREAD

	C	P	F
⅓ cup corn meal, finely ground	38	4	1
⅓ cup wheat germ	24	13	5
⅓ cup whole-wheat flour	28	5	1
1 egg, beaten		7	6
¼ cup milk	3	2	3
1 teaspoon baking powder			
¼ teaspoon salt			

Combine dry ingredients and mix well. Add milk and then egg. Mix well and pour into preheated lightly greased pan. Bake at 375° for about 15 minutes or until well browned. Serves four.

One serving contains 23 grams of carbohydrate, 8 grams of protein, 4 grams of fat, and 160 calories. This may be substituted for one and one-half bread exchanges and one meat exchange.

COMMENT. If much corn bread is eaten, it is important to add some wheat flour, preferably wheat germ, to the batter, since corn meal is deficient in several B vitamins that are supplied by wheat. In many parts of the South corn bread may be eaten twice daily, and in these cases it should certainly be enriched with whole-wheat flour.

This bread is especially good when served with leafy green vegetables. It complements the flavor of baked or poached fish and is unsurpassed when served hot with buttermilk.

TOMATO YEAST BREAD

	C	P	F
1 package dry yeast	4	4	
1 cup tomato juice	10	2	
1 tablespoon caraway seed			
1 tablespoon corn oil			14
1 teaspoon salt			
1 cup rye flour	62	8	1
2 cups white flour	167	23	2

Mix yeast with 1 cup white flour and salt. Place tomato juice, oil, and caraway seed in a large bowl. Add yeast and white flour mixture. Stir until free of lumps, then beat for 2 minutes at slow speed on mixer or 200 strokes by hand. Add 1 cup rye flour and mix well. Then add remaining cup of white flour. Dough should be very stiff at this point. Turn out on a floured board and knead until smooth (2 to 3 minutes). Divide into two parts and shape into long narrow loaves. Let rise in a warm (85 to 95°) place until almost doubled in bulk. Bake at 375° for 25 to 30 minutes.

The entire recipe contains 243 grams of carbohydrate, 37 grams of protein, 17 grams of fat, and 1275 calories. It can be counted just as ordinary bread in the diet. A 25-gram slice may be substituted for one bread exchange.

BRAN MUFFINS

	C	P	F
1/4 cup wheat germ	10	6	2
1/4 cup whole-wheat flour	21	4	1
1/2 cup 100 percent bran	19	3	1
1/4 teaspoon salt			
1 1/2 teaspoon baking powder			
1/2 cup milk	6	4	5
1 1/2 tablespoon corn oil			21
1 egg, lightly beaten		7	6
1/4 cup raisins	30		

Mix all dry ingredients until well blended. Add raisins and continue to mix until raisins are coated. Add egg, milk, and oil and let stand briefly. Oil six muffin cups, fill two-thirds full, and bake at 400° for 20 to 30 minutes. Makes six muffins.

Each muffin contains about 14 grams of carbohydrate, 4 grams of protein, 6 grams of fat, and 125 calories. This may be substituted for one bread exchange and one fat exchange.

SCOTTISH OAT CAKES

	C	P	F
1½ cups instant oats	36	9	1
¼ cup corn meal	28	3	
¼ cup unsaturated margarine			46
½ cup whole-wheat flour	41	8	1
½ teaspoon salt			
¼ teaspoon baking soda			
½ teaspoon baking powder			
⅓ cup boiling water			

Mix all ingredients except water until thoroughly blended. Add boiling water and stir quickly to mix. Turn out on a floured board, roll about ⅛ to ¼ inch thick, and cut into rounds using a biscuit cutter. Bake on a lightly greased baking sheet at 350° for 30 to 40 minutes.

Total recipe contains 105 grams of carbohydrate, 20 grams of protein, 48 grams of fat, and 930 calories. Divide these figures by the number of cakes to determine approximate content of each cake.

PANCAKES

	C	P	F
⅓ cup whole-wheat flour, sifted	27	4	
½ teaspoon baking soda			
1 teaspoon baking powder			
¼ teaspoon salt			
⅓ cup quick-cooking oatmeal	18	4	2
⅓ cup whole bran	13	3	1
2 tablespoons wheat germ	5	3	1
1 egg, slightly beaten		7	6
1 tablespoon oil			14
1 cup buttermilk	12	8	

Sift first four ingredients together; add remaining dry ingredients and mix well. Mix oil, buttermilk, and egg; add all at once to dry ingredients. Mix well. Bake on Teflon griddle set at medium heat. Makes ten pancakes.

Entire recipe contains 75 grams of carbohydrate, 29 grams of protein, 24 grams of fat, and 630 calories. Use an equal amount of batter for each pancake and divide the total figures by the number of pancakes to determine the content of each pancake. When the recipe is divided into ten equal-sized pancakes, two pancakes may be substituted for one bread exchange and one fat exchange.

CHEESE PANCAKES

	C	P	F
½ cup uncreamed cottage cheese	3	23	
¼ cup evaporated skim milk	6	4	
¼ teaspoon baking powder			
1 egg		7	6
2 tablespoons white flour	12	2	
½ pint low-fat yogurt	13	8	4
½ pint strawberries (fresh, canned, or frozen, unsweetened)	11	1	

Blend cheese and milk until smooth. Add baking powder, egg, and flour and blend well. Pour 1 tablespoon of batter for each pancake onto a moderately hot Teflon griddle. When brown on both sides, remove to a hot plate to keep warm. Makes about sixteen pancakes.

Sweeten strawberries to taste with a noncaloric sweetener. On each pancake place 1 tablespoon strawberries and 1 tablespoon yogurt. Roll the pancake to enclose mixture and serve immediately.

Each filled pancake contains 3 grams of carbohydrate, 3 grams of protein, 1 gram of fat, and 30 calories. Two pancakes may be substituted for one-half bread exchange and one-half meat exchange.

ANGELA'S SUNDAY WAFFLES

	C	P	F
1 package yeast	1	1	
½ cup warm milk	6	4	5
1 teaspoon dark molasses	4		
¼ teaspoon salt			
1 tablespoon oil			14
¼ cup wheat germ	18	10	4
1 egg		7	6
¼ cup whole-wheat flour	21	4	1
1 tablespoon powdered skim milk	2	1	
¼ cup pecans, chopped	4	3	22

Dissolve yeast in warm milk; add molasses, egg yolk, salt, oil, and wheat germ. Stir until well mixed. Add flour, nuts, and powdered milk. Beat egg white until stiff and fold into batter. Bake on a hot waffle iron. Serves two.

One serving contains 28 grams of carbohydrate, 15 grams of protein, 26 grams of fat, and 405 calories. This may be substituted for two bread, one meat, and four fat exchanges.

COMMENT. This is a delicious waffle and very nutritious. One serving contains calcium, phosphorus, vitamin E, iron, and B vitamins. Serve with crushed fresh fruit or sugar-free syrup.

SALLY LUNN

	C	P	F
1 package dry yeast	4	4	
3 cups white flour	250	35	3
1 cup milk	12	8	10
2 eggs		14	12
½ teaspoon salt			
1 tablespoon sugar	12		
½-cup unsaturated margarine			92

Cream margarine, salt, and sugar. Beat eggs and add to margarine. Mix well. Combine dry yeast and flour and mix thoroughly. Add flour mixture alternately with milk to margarine mixture. When well mixed, pour into oiled tube pan. Let rise 1½ hours or until doubled in bulk. Bake at 350° for 45 to 50 minutes. Serve hot, preferably with margarine and coffee.

Entire recipe contains 278 grams of carbohydrate, 60 grams of protein, 117 grams of fat, and 2410 calories. Divide these figures by number of equal-sized slices to determine content of each slice. Carbohydrate content is about the same as for ordinary bread, but fat content is about four times as high.

CHRISTMAS CAKE

	C	P	F
1 cup pecans, coarsely chopped	11	9	73
¼ cup white raisins	28	1	
½ cup white flour	42	6	1
¼ cup sugar	50		
1 egg		7	6
¼ teaspoon baking powder			
2 tablespoons margarine			23
2 tablespoons bourbon			

Cream sugar and margarine. Add eggs and bourbon and beat well. Dredge nuts and raisins in flour. Add excess flour to margarine mix; then add nuts and raisins. Mix until just blended. Pour into well-oiled pan and bake at 325° for about 45 minutes or until a toothpick comes out clean. Slice into very thin slices and serve as fruit cake.

Total recipe contains 131 grams of carbohydrate, 23 grams of protein, and 103 grams of fat.

COMMENT. Dark raisins can be used but the final cake is not as attractive. Contents must be calculated from weight of finished cake. The maneuvers are as follows:

1. Weigh cake.
2. Divide 131 grams of carbohydrate, 23 grams of protein, 103 grams of fat by weight of cake.
3. Weigh slice to be served diabetic.
4. Multiply (3) times the product of (2). This will give the figures for the diabetic serving.

This is a simpler but less accurate method:
1. Slice cake into *equal* sized servings (makes about 10 small slices).
2. Divide C, P, and F figures by total number of slices to obtain content of each slice.

This is a more precise but complicated method:
1. Weigh cake (remembering that entire cake contains 131 C, 23 P, and 103 F).
2. Weigh slice to be served.
3. Divide weight of slice to be served by weight of entire cake, and multiply by the C, P, and F figures above to obtain the amount of C, P, and F in the weighed slice.

Example:
1. Suppose entire cake weighs 20 ounces.
2. Each slice to be served weighs 2 ounces.
3. 2 ounces divided by 20 ounces = 0.1 (or 1/10)

then 131 grams of carbohydrate × 0.1 = 13.1 grams of carbohydrate
23 grams of protein × 0.1 = 2.3 grams of protein
and 103 grams of fat × 0.1 = 10.3 grams of fat

Therefore a 2-ounce serving provides 13.1 grams of carbohydrate, 2 to 3 grams of protein, and 10.3 grams of fat.

OATMEAL COOKIES

	C	P	F
1½ cups oatmeal	80	17	9
⅔ cup melted margarine			122
4 egg whites, slightly beaten	1	14	
2½ teaspoons Sucaryl			
1½ cups flour, sifted	125	17	2
½ teaspoon salt			
2 teaspoons baking powder			
½ cup skim milk	6	4	
1 teaspoon vanilla			
½ cup raisins	61	2	
½ cup walnuts, chopped	8	9	37

Mix oatmeal and margarine. Blend in eggs and Sucaryl. Add dry ingredients alternately with milk and vanilla. Add raisins and nuts. Drop by level tablespoonfuls on cookie sheet. Bake in hot (375°) oven for 10 to 15 minutes. Makes about four dozen.

Total recipe contains 281 grams of carbohydrate, 63 grams of protein, and 170 grams of fat. If an equal amount is used for each cookie, the content of one cookie can be determined by dividing the total figures by the number of cookies.

CINNAMON COOKIES

	C	P	F
5 tablespoons margarine			57
1 cup flour, sifted	84	12	1
1/4 teaspoon baking powder			
1 1/2 tablespoons Sucaryl			
2 teaspoons vanilla			
1 tablespoon milk	1	1	1
1 teaspoon cinnamon			

Cream margarine until light. Blend in flour and other dry ingredients. Combine Sucaryl, vanilla, and milk. Stir into flour and mix well. Measure dough into level tablespoonfuls and flatten into shape with a fork. Bake at 375° for 12 to 15 minutes or until brown.

Total recipe contains 85 grams of carbohydrate, 13 grams of protein, and 59 grams of fat. Divide total figures by number of cookies to determine content of each.

SHORTCAKE

	C	P	F
2 cups flour, sifted	167	26	2
2 tablespoons sugar	24		
3 teaspoons baking powder			
1 teaspoon salt			
6 tablespoons margarine			68
2/3 cup skim milk	8	6	

Sift dry ingredients together. Cut in 5 tablespoons of margarine until first crumbles form. Add milk and stir lightly. Turn out on floured board and knead until smooth. Divide into two parts.

Fit one part into 8-inch pie pan. Use reserved tablespoon of margarine to coat top of this part; then fit the remaining dough on top. Bake at 450° for 15 minutes. Separate layers when done. Makes eight servings.

Each serving contains approximately 25 grams of carbohydrate, 4 grams of protein, 9 grams of fat, and 200 calories. This can be substituted for one and one-half bread exchanges and two fat exchanges.

COMMENT. Strawberries, blueberries, raspberries, peaches, etc. can be used with this bread for conventional shortcakes. Don't forget to add figures for the fruit and whipped topping, if used. Obtain values from Table 2.

Fruit-based Desserts

PAPAYA AND BLUEBERRIES

	C	P	F
2 fresh papayas (180 grams each, prepared)	33	2	
1 lime	9		
2 ounces blueberries	8		

Cut papayas into halves lengthwise and scoop out seeds. Remove outer peel. Sprinkle all surfaces with juice of lime. Chill well. When ready to serve, drain excess lime juice into small container. Fill papaya cavities with fresh or frozen (unsweetened) blueberries and sprinkle berries with drained lime juice. Serves four.

One serving contains 12 grams of carbohydrate, 48 calories, and vitamins A and C. This amount may be substituted for one fruit exchange.

COMMENT. This is a colorful and tasty dessert. If papaya is not available, cantaloupe or honeydew melon can be substituted. Frozen berries are not nearly as good as fresh, but will do. The papayas can be prepared several hours in advance. All desserts should be as easy and nutritious as this one.

STRAWBERRY SPONGE

	C	P	F
1 envelope unflavored gelatin		7	
½ cup cold water			
1 tablespoon Sucaryl solution			
1½ tablespoons lemon juice	1		
1 pint strawberries, crushed	22	2	
2 egg whites		7	

Soften gelatin in water in top of double boiler. Add Sucaryl and lemon juice; heat, stirring until gelatin dissolves. Remove from heat and add crushed berries. Let stand until mixture begins to thicken; then beat until light and fluffy. Beat egg whites until stiff; fold into gelatin mixture. Spoon into six individual molds or into a large 3-cup mold, lightly oiled. Chill until firm. Serves six.

One serving contains 4 grams of carbohydrate, 3 grams of protein, and 30 calories. It may be substituted for one-half fruit exchange.

FROU-FROU

	C	P	F
1 pint low-fat yogurt	24	16	8
4 tablespoons sugar-free jelly or jam, any flavor (10 percent carbohydrate)	8		

Thoroughly mix ingredients and serve in sherbet glasses, well chilled. Serves four.

A serving of ½ cup contains 8 grams of carbohydrate, 4 grams of protein, 2 grams of fat, about 65 calories, calcium, phosphorus, and B vitamins. This may be substituted for one-half milk exchange.

COMMENT. If fresh fruit and artificial sweetener are used instead of the jelly recommended above, vitamin C and usually vitamin A are added. This is a pleasantly tart dessert that is easy on the calorie counters.

FRESH FRUIT WHIP

	C	P	F
3 egg whites		10	
¼ cup powdered skim milk	8	5	
Liquid sweetener			
1 cup fresh fruit, crushed			

Whip egg whites until they stand in stiff peaks. Add powdered milk, 1 tablespoon at a time. Add artificial sweetener to taste. Add crushed fruit and continue beating at high speed until mixture stands in stiff peaks. Chill in freezer at least 1 hour before serving. Makes eight servings of ½ cup each.

A ½-cup serving contains about 5 grams of carbohydrate, 2 grams of protein, and 30 calories if raspberries, strawberries, blackberries, peaches, or apricots are used. This may be substituted for one-half fruit exchange.

COMMENT. This dessert tastes better if the fruit is somewhat tart. Raspberries and apricots both make outstanding desserts. Use whatever is plentiful and alter the calculations according to the amount of fruit used.

GRAPEFRUIT CHIFFON

	C	P	F
1 medium grapefruit	22	1	
1 package strawberry D-Zerta		6	
1½ cups grapefruit juice	35	2	
3 eggs, separated		21	18
¼ cup powdered skim milk	8	5	
¼ teaspoon grated lemon peel			
¼ cup lemon juice	5		
¼ teaspoon cream of tartar			

Remove grapefruit sections and place in colander to drain. Heat 1 cup of grapefruit juice to boiling and use to dissolve gelatin. Beat egg yolks and combine in pan with remaining ½ cup grapefruit juice, lemon juice, lemon peel; cook over low heat, stirring constantly. When mixture lightly covers spoon, remove from heat and stir into gelatin mixture. Be sure gelatin is completely dissolved. Chill until mixture will mound on a spoon but is not yet solid. Beat egg whites with cream of tartar until frothy; add ¼ cup powdered skim milk and gradually continue beating until stiff peaks form. Beat gelatin mixture until light and frothy. Fold in grapefruit sections, then egg-white mixture. Put in serving dishes and chill until firm. This will take several hours. Makes six servings of ½ cup each.

One serving contains 12 grams of carbohydrate, 6 grams of protein, 3 grams of fat, and 100 calories. This may be substituted for one fruit and one meat exchanges.

COMMENT. The above combination can also be used as a pie filling. This is not encouraged because of the high fat content of pastry and the enormous increase in calories. For example, if the ½-cup serving recommended above were taken on a slice of average pie crust, the content would be 26 grams of carbohydrate, 8 grams of protein, 12 grams of fat, and 245 calories.

PEACH PARFAIT

	C	P	F
½ cup peach purée	11		
2 tablespoons cornstarch	14		
½ cup water			
2 tablespoons lemon juice	2		
Liquid sweetener			
4 cups sliced peaches	61	4	
3 ounces Neufchâtel cheese	3	8	20
¼ cup Sweetness & Light	10		

Combine peach purée, cornstarch, water, and lemon juice. Boil and stir until thick and clear. Add liquid sweetener to taste (you will need about the equivalent of ⅔ cup sugar) and set aside to cool. Blend cheese and artificial sugar until smooth and light. Layer cheese, purée, and peach slices in parfait glasses and chill before serving. If there is a time lag between preparation and serving, sprinkle additional lemon juice over peach slices to prevent browning. Serves eight.

One serving contains 13 grams of carbohydrate, 2 grams of protein, 3 grams of fat, and 85 calories. This may be substituted for one fruit and one-half fat exchanges.

COMMENT. The cheese mixture can be stretched by blending several tablespoons of evaporated skim milk with it. This also makes it easier to spread in the parfait glasses. Three ounces of cheese will easily blend with ½ cup of evaporated skim milk. If this amount is used, increase figures for the total recipe by 12 grams of carbohydrate, 8 grams of protein, and 80 calories. Divide these figures by eight to get the content of one serving.

AVOCADO DESSERT

	C	P	F
1 large ripe avocado	9	4	33
Juice of 1 lime	9		
Liquid sweetener to taste			

Combine all ingredients and mix in blender until quite smooth. Put in sherbet cups and chill well. Garnish with chopped nuts or thin slice of lime. Serves two generously.

One serving contains 9 grams of carbohydrate, 2 grams of protein, 16 grams of fat, and 185 calories. It is obviously not for weight watchers. One serving may be substituted for one fruit and three fat exchanges.

FRUIT FLOAT

	C	P	F
1 cup strawberries	11		
Liquid sweetener to taste			
1 cup whole milk	12	8	10

Blend strawberries in a blender until well puréed; add sweetener and milk and mix thoroughly. Makes 1 serving.

Contains 23 grams of carbohydrate, 8 grams of protein, 10 grams of fat, and 214 calories. This may be substituted for one fruit and one milk exchanges.

COMMENT. This is an especially good warm weather drink for children and active adults. It is often successful in getting milk down when other methods fail. It can be made richer by using 1 cup of evaporated milk instead of fresh. In this case, double the carbohydrate, protein, and fat contributed by the milk above and increase the milk exchange to two instead of one. This may also be used as part of an emergency diet.

PEACH FLOAT

	C	P	F
1 medium peach	10		
1 tablespoon lemon juice	1		
¾ cup whole milk	9	6	8
Liquid sweetener			

Purée peach and lemon juice in a blender. When quite liquid, add milk and liquid sweetener to taste. Mix well and serve immediately. Serves one.

Contains 20 grams of carbohydrate, 6 grams of protein, 8 grams of fat, and 175 calories. This may be substituted for one fruit exchange and three-fourths milk exchange.

COMMENT. Many fruit combinations can be used and the calculations are simple. All can be topped with a tablespoon of vanilla ice cream or whipped cream of some kind. If you add this, don't forget to include it in your calculations. This drink may be used as part of an emergency diet.

CREAM PUFFS

	C	P	F
¼ cup unsaturated margarine			45
½ cup boiling water			
½ cup flour, sifted	42	6	1
Pinch of salt			
2 large eggs		14	12

Cut margarine into small pieces and add to boiling water. Stir to dissolve completely. When mixture is boiling vigorously, add flour and salt. Keep heat low and stir batter rapidly with wooden spoon. When batter pulls away from sides of pan, remove from heat and beat in eggs, one at a time. When well mixed, drop by spoonfuls (make amount of dough in each as equal as possible) onto greased cookie sheet and bake in a very hot (450°) oven for 10 minutes. Reduce heat to 400° and continue baking until puffs are firm and brown on top. There should be no beads of moisture on surface. (Takes about 25 minutes.) Cool on wire rack. When cool, cut each puff in half and fill with Cream-Puff Filling (recipe follows). Makes about six large puffs.

Each *unfilled* puff contains 7 grams of carbohydrate, 3 grams of protein, 10 grams of fat, and 130 calories. Each equals one-half bread and two fat exchanges.

CREAM-PUFF FILLING

	C	P	F
2 egg whites		7	
¼ cup powdered skim milk	8	5	
Liquid sweetener			
1 cup strawberries	11		

Beat egg whites until they stand in stiff peaks; add powdered milk, 1 tablespoon at a time and continue to beat. Add liquid sweetener to taste and then add strawberries. Beat until well mixed and quite stiff. Divide equally to fill six cream puffs. Sprinkle with teaspoon of Sweetness & Light or Sweet'n Low.

Filling for one puff contains 3 grams of carbohydrate, 2 grams of protein, and 20 calories. This may be substituted for one-half fruit exchange.

COMMENT. Each *filled* puff contains 10 grams of carbohydrate, 5 grams of protein, 10 grams of fat, and 150 calories. This may be substituted for one-half bread, one-half fruit, and two fat exchanges.

BANANA CREAM PIE

	C	P	F
½ cup evaporated skim milk	12	8	
3 eggs		21	18
Dash of salt			
¾ teaspoon vanilla			
1¼ cups fresh skim milk	15	10	
⅓ cup Sweetness & Light	13		
1 cup sliced bananas	33	2	
1 tablespoon lemon juice	1		

Beat eggs with salt and evaporated milk until well mixed. Add fresh milk and Sweetness & Light. Cook in top of double boiler until mixture is consistency of soft custard. Add vanilla, mix well, and remove from heat. Toss sliced bananas with lemon juice and arrange in bottom of 9-inch graham cracker crust (recipe follows), reserving several slices for garnish. Pour custard mix over the bananas. Arrange reserved slices on top and chill until well set.

GRAHAM CRACKER CRUST

	C	P	F
1½ cups fine graham cracker crumbs	113	10	17
4 tablespoons margarine			45

Mix well and press into 9-inch pie plate. Use another plate of equal size to pack crumbs firmly. Chill or freeze until ready to use. Serves eight.

Each slice contains approximately 23 grams of carbohydrate, 6 grams of protein, 10 grams of fat, and 205 calories. This approximates one bread, one-half milk, and one fat exchanges.

COMMENT. The basic recipe can be used for almost any cream pie. For coconut cream pie, use 1½ cups freshly grated coconut (prepared coconut usually has sugar added) instead of the bananas. Mix 1 cup of coconut with the cream base and use the remaining ½ cup to garnish the top. Those who can have saturated fat only in extremely limited amounts should not use the variation because of the high saturated fat content of coconut.

One slice of coconut cream pie contains about 22 grams of carbohydrate, 7 grams of protein, 16 grams of fat, and 260 calories. This may be used instead of one bread, one-half milk, and two fat exchanges.

Jellies and Syrups

There are many excellent sugar-free jellies, jams, and syrups available commercially, and unless large amounts are eaten it is probably as economical to buy as to make them. Since sugar-free jellies must be refrigerated, make only as much as will be used in a week or two. The juices can, of course, be frozen when available and thawed for later use.

GRAPE JELLY

	C	P	F
1 tablespoon gelatin		9	
1½ cups grape juice, unsweetened	60	1	
1 tablespoon Sucaryl solution			

Soften gelatin in ¼ cup grape juice. Bring remaining juice to boiling and add gelatin to dissolve. Add Sucaryl. Stir until gelatin is dissolved. Cool and store in refrigerator.

Total volume contains 60 grams of carbohydrate and 10 grams of protein.

COMMENT. Virtually any fruit juice can be used in the recipe above. To make jams, simply include fruit as part of the total volume.

WILD BLACKBERRY SYRUP

	C	P	F
1 quart blackberries	51		
1 tablespoon Sucaryl solution			
1 tablespoon lemon juice	1		

Put berries in a large kettle with lemon juice. Heat slowly to boiling and cook for 3 to 5 minutes. Strain through several layers of cheesecloth or a fine wire strainer. Discard seeds and pulp. Add Sucaryl to taste. Serve over pancakes and waffles. Makes about 1 pint of liquid.

Total volume contains about 50 grams of carbohydrate.

COMMENT. If berries are not very tart increase the lemon juice to achieve the desired flavor.

CHAPTER 7

Vegetables

It is ironic that the group A or low-carbohydrate vegetables are among the least enjoyed by many families. An especially large portion of this chapter is devoted to recipes for preparing these vegetables. Many of them are excellent sources of vitamins and minerals and should be used daily in diets for the whole family as well as the diabetic member.

Leafy Green Vegetables

Outside the southeastern part of this country, greens are rarely eaten except in salads. This is unfortunate as many of them are quite tasty and all are excellent sources of vitamin A and the B complex group. The following basic recipe is suitable for cooking most greens. The commonest error is to overcook. When this occurs, the color changes from a bright green to a yellowish green and the flavor becomes much stronger and somewhat altered. If you've never eaten a cooked green vegetable except canned or frozen spinach, you have a pleasant surprise in store. If the greens are young and tender, which they rarely are unless you either grow your own or shop in an Oriental market area, they will cook completely in less than 3 minutes. If they are tough, cooking will take somewhat longer, but never longer than 10 minutes. Because of the very low calorie content of greens, it is possible to use larger amounts of fat and other seasoning sauces than is practical with many other vegetables. In these recipes the fat content has been kept as low as is possible without altering the flavor of the finished dish unnecessarily. If your diet permits additional fat, by all means use it, but remember to increase the calories accordingly. If your diet requires the use of extra unsaturated fat, most of the cooked vegetables here—especially the greens and squashes—make an ideal vehicle. To avoid altered flavor, add oil immediately before serving. Remember that 1 teaspoon of fat carries 45 calories and 5 grams of fat, and is equal to one fat exchange.

COOKED GREENS

Wash, but do not shake, one bunch of greens for each two members of your family. Heat a heavy pan and add 1 teaspoon cooking oil or bacon drippings for each bunch of greens. Add the greens and cook quickly, stirring every minute or so. Salt to taste and set off heat when they are well wilted but not overdone. Let set in covered pan for 5 to 10 minutes. They will continue to cook a bit after you've removed them from the heat. Serve with corn bread and fish or pork.

If fat intake is very limited, count one-half fat exchange, or 2.5 grams, for each serving. Each serving contains about 35 calories.

MOM'S TURNIP GREENS

Cut turnip roots into quarters and simmer in ¼ cup water and ½ teaspoon salt. Wash greens and remove tough stems while roots are cooking. About 5 minutes before serving time add greens and continue simmering for 5 minutes. Add extra salt, if necessary, and 1 teaspoon bacon drippings or other fat before serving. Garnish with black pepper.

The greens contain negligible carbohydrate, protein, fat, and calories. A ½ cup serving of the roots contains 7 grams of carbohydrate, 2 grams of protein, and 35 calories. This amount may be substituted for one group B vegetable exchange. The greens are rich in A and B vitamins as well as iron.

GREEN CELERY

	C	P	F
2 cups outside celery stalks and leaves	6	2	
½ cup milk	6	4	5
½ teaspoon salt			

Slice celery diagonally. Cook milk, salt, and celery stalks in top of double boiler for 5 minutes. Add chopped celery leaves and cook 3 minutes longer. Garnish with paprika.

A ½-cup serving contains negligible carbohydrate, protein, and fat, and about 30 calories. This amount may be substituted for one group A vegetable exchange.

CARAWAY CABBAGE

Shred 4 cups cabbage. Heat heavy pan very hot and add 1 teaspoon bacon drippings or other fat; add cabbage and stir briskly for 1 to 2 minutes. Add 1 tablespoon caraway seeds and stir in. Remove from heat and let stand covered 5 minutes. Taste for salt, adding extra if needed. Serves six.

One serving contains 3 grams of carbohydrate, 1 gram of protein, 1 gram of fat, about 25 calories, and vitamins A and C. This amount may be substituted for one group A vegetable exchange.

BOK CHOY
(Chinese Cabbage)

	C	P	F
2 cups bok choy, diagonally sliced	4	1	
2 cups chicken stock		8	
1 small onion, diced	6	1	
⅛ teaspoon pepper			
1½ teaspoon salt			

Heat stock and seasonings to boiling; add bok choy, cover pot, and turn off heat. Remove cover occasionally to test. The bok should be crisp but tender. Serve with French dressing or plain. The broth can be served separately as clear soup.

One cup of broth or one-half cup of vegetable contains vitamins

A and B and trace minerals, but negligible carbohydrate, protein, and fat. Consider only the dressing used.

COMMENT. This makes a good filler dish to combine with meats and other high-calorie entrées. It also combines well with Italian-style casseroles such as lasagne. This permits more calories, carbohydrate, and fat to be taken in the main dish.

SESAME CHARD

Wash about 1 pound Swiss chard and remove stems. Chop into bite sized pieces. Heat a large, heavy pan moderately hot, and add 1 teaspoon margarine. Stir-fry chard about 2 minutes or until just well wilted. Season with salt and garnish heavily with toasted sesame seeds. Makes four servings.

This is a good source of vitamins A and B and iron. A ½-cup serving contains 4 grams of carbohydrate, 2 grams of protein, 1 gram of fat, and 35 calories, and may be substituted for one group A vegetable exchange.

Stir-fried Mixed Vegetables

When families are confronted with strange vegetables for the first time, it usually requires some salesmanship even to get the dish tasted, let alone eaten. The Chinese custom of blending several vegetables in one dish often lets a new vegetable pass almost unnoticed. The cooking method, called "stir-frying," is much as described above. It involves using a heavy pan with a small amount of fat. Vegetables are added according to length of cooking time required and stirred constantly while they fry in the hot pan. The vegetables are seared and carmelized by the high heat, adding a pleasantly different flavor. Mixtures are limited only by your imagination and the caloric restrictions in your diet. Several recipes are included below as examples. If it's an especially hectic day, leftover meat, fowl, or fish can be added at the last minute for a one-dish meal. If the fat content of your diet is limited, try this method of cooking either fresh or frozen vegetables. If you're trying a new vegetable, make up the remainder of the dish from familiar things. The family is less likely to balk this way.

The dishes appear more interesting if the colors are mixed and if the vegetables are sliced diagonally.

MUSHROOMS AND ASPARAGUS

	C	P	F
½ pound fresh mushrooms, diagonally sliced	8	6	
2 cups asparagus, diagonally sliced	9	7	
1 teaspoon oil			5

Heat pan; add 1 teaspoon oil, then add asparagus. Stir-fry 1 to 2 minutes; add mushrooms and continue to stir for 2 more minutes. Add salt and pepper to taste. Serves four.

A ½-cup serving contains 4 grams of carbohydrate, 3 grams of protein, 1 gram of fat, and 35 calories. This amount may be substituted for one group A vegetable exchange.

SQUASH AND MUSHROOMS

	C	P	F
1 pound summer squash	16	5	
1 small onion, finely chopped	6	1	
1 tablespoon unsaturated margarine			11
¼ cup green pepper, chopped	1		
½ teaspoon salt			
½ teaspoon black pepper (this may be too much unless you're a pepper fan)			
¼ pound mushrooms	4	3	
¼ teaspoon dried dill weed			

Heat margarine in heavy skillet until hot; add sliced squash, mushrooms, and onion and sauté 2 to 3 minutes, uncovered. Add seasonings, cover, and cook for 5 to 6 minutes, keeping the heat rather high. Add green pepper and serve. Serves six.

Each serving contains 4 grams of carbohydrate, 2 grams of protein, 2 grams of fat, 40 calories, and vitamins A, B, and C. This amount may be substituted for one group A vegetable exchange and one-half fat exchange.

COMMENT. For low-fat or restricted-calorie diets, this can be prepared in a Teflon skillet without the margarine. In this case, one serving contains 4 grams of carbohydrate, 2 grams of protein, no fat, and 25 calories. A serving may substitute for one group A vegetable exchange only.

MUSHROOMS AND PEAPODS

	C	P	F
½ pound fresh mushrooms, diagonally sliced	8	6	
1 cup celery, diagonally sliced	3	1	
½ pound edible peapods with stems removed (or 10-ounce package frozen)	24	7	
1 tablespoon soy sauce	2		
1 teaspoon grated fresh ginger or ¼ teaspoon powdered ginger			
1 teaspoon cooking oil			5

Heat heavy pan very hot and add oil. Add peapods first (if frozen, allow to cook until thawed before adding next vegetable), then celery, and finally, mushrooms (if canned mushrooms are used, add when cooking is completed and allow only to heat through). Stir-fry about 2 minutes after mushrooms are added. Lower heat to lowest setting and add soy sauce and ginger. Let simmer 2 to 3 minutes longer. Serve at once.

A ½-cup serving contains 7 grams of carbohydrate, 2 grams of protein, 1 gram of fat, and 45 calories. This amount may be substituted for one group B vegetable exchange.

RED AND WHITE

	C	P	F
1 large red pepper, diced (about ½ cup)	3	1	
2 cups cauliflower buds and leaves, cut into ½-inch diagonal slices	8	5	
1½ cups celery, diagonally sliced	5	1	
1 teaspoon oil			5
Dash of liquid hot pepper			
½ teaspoon salt			

Heat pan and add oil. Add celery, then cauliflower, and then pepper. Stir-fry for 3 to 4 minutes. Add seasonings and set off heat. Let stand covered another 3 to 4 minutes. All vegetables should remain crisp. Serves four.

A ½-cup serving contains 4 grams of carbohydrate, 2 grams of protein, 1 gram of fat, and about 35 calories. This amount may be substituted for one group A vegetable exchange.

BROCCOLI AND MUSHROOMS

	C	P	F
1 large green pepper	3	1	
2 cups celery, diagonally sliced	6	2	
2 cups broccoli, diagonally sliced	9	5	
2 cups (about ½ pound) mushrooms, diagonally sliced	8	6	
⅛ teaspoon garlic powder			
⅛ teaspoon curry powder			
½ teaspoon salt			
1 teaspoon oil			5
1 tablespoon lemon juice or cider vinegar			

Heat pan; add oil, then celery, broccoli, mushrooms, and pepper. Stir-fry for 3 to 4 minutes. Add seasonings and lemon juice or cider vinegar and turn off heat. Let stand 3 to 4 minutes longer. Serves four to six generously.

A ½-cup serving contains about 4 grams of carbohydrate, 2 grams of protein, 1 gram of fat, 35 calories, and vitamins A and C. This amount may be substituted for one group A vegetable exchange.

EGGPLANT AND TOMATO

	C	P	F
1 eggplant, unpeeled and diced	15	4	
½ teaspoon salt			
1 tablespoon cooking oil			14
1 small onion, chopped	5	1	
Dash of pepper			
½ teaspoon dried basil			
2 large tomatoes, peeled and diced	17	4	1

Put oil in heavy frying pan with cover; add eggplant and onion and sauté 4 to 5 minutes. Add salt, pepper, and basil; cook covered 10 minutes. Add tomatoes and cook uncovered 5 minutes, stirring occasionally. Raise heat during last minute of cooking to evaporate excess moisture. Garnish with Parmesan cheese. Makes about four servings.

Each ½ cup contains 9 grams of carbohydrate, 2 grams of protein, 4 grams of fat, and 80 calories. This amount may be substituted for one group B vegetable exchange and one fat exchange.

DILLED CABBAGE AND BEANS

	C	P	F
8 cups shredded cabbage	37	10	
1 teaspoon oil			5
1½ cups French green beans	12	3	
½ teaspoon dried dill weed			
¼ teaspoon salt			

Heat oil in heavy pan; add all ingredients and stir quickly until cabbage is slightly wilted. Cover and steam for 5 more minutes. Add additional water (not more than 2 or 3 tablespoons) if vegetables appear dry. Serves six.

A 1-cup serving contains 8 grams of carbohydrate, 2 grams of protein, 1 gram of fat, about 50 calories, and vitamins A, B, and C. This amount may be substituted for one group B vegetable exchange.

Eggplant, Carrots, Squash, Potato

BROILED EGGPLANT

Slice a large eggplant crosswise about ¾ inch thick. Brush each side with margarine and sprinkle with salt, pepper, and paprika. Broil 6 to 8 minutes on each side. Liquid smoke adds flavor.

Two slices contain approximately 5 grams of carbohydrate, 1 gram of protein, 3 grams of fat, and 50 calories. This amount may be substituted for one group A vegetable exchange and one-half fat exchange.

MOM'S EGGPLANT
(from the kitchen of Mrs. L. W. Middleton)

	C	P	F
1 large eggplant	15	4	
1 teaspoon pork sausage seasoning with sage			
2 tablespoons flour	12	2	
1 teaspoon oil			5

Peel and slice eggplant. Simmer until tender in ¼ cup water in covered pan. Add flour and seasoning and stir until smooth. Add extra salt and pepper if necessary; the mixture should be quite spicy with a distinct flavor of sage. Heat well-seasoned cast-iron or other heavy griddle to about pancake-cooking temperature. Drop mixture by spoonfuls onto oiled griddle and brown like pancakes. Serves four.

One serving contains 7 grams of carbohydrate, 1 gram of protein, 1 gram of fat, and 40 calories. This amount may be substituted for one group B vegetable exchange.

ZUCCHINI

	C	P	F
1 tablespoon unsaturated margarine			11
1½ cups celery, chopped	5	1	
1 cup onion, chopped	12	2	
3 cups zucchini, sliced	11	3	
¼ cup chicken stock		1	
¼ cup cooking sherry	5		
Salt to taste			

Sauté celery and onion in margarine; add chicken broth and zucchini. Simmer for barely 5 minutes. Zucchini should still be crisp. Add sherry and salt before serving. Yields about 5 cups.

A ½-cup serving contains about 25 calories, 3 grams of carbohydrate, 1 gram of protein, and 1 gram of fat. This amount may be substituted for one group A vegetable exchange.

This dish is considerably more flavorful with additional fat, and if your diet permits, by all means increase the fat, but don't forget to increase also the amount of calories and fat in your calculations.

GINGERED CARROTS

	C	P	F
4 cups carrots, cut into ⅛-inch diagonal slices	40	6	
1 teaspoon oil			5
1 tablespoon (10 grams) crystallized ginger	9		
2 tablespoons wine vinegar	2		
¼ teaspoon salt			
⅛ teaspoon garlic powder			
2 tablespoons parsley, chopped	1		

Heat oil in heavy pan and add carrots. Stir-fry for 1 to 2 minutes. Add remaining ingredients; cover and cook over low heat for about 15 minutes or until carrots are tender. Serves six.

A ½-cup serving contains 9 grams of carbohydrate, 1 gram of protein, 1 gram of fat, 50 calories, and a large amount of vitamin A. This amount may be substituted for one group B vegetable exchange.

MIXED SQUASH

	C	P	F
3 small zucchini	11	3	
3 small crookneck squash	11	3	
¼ cup boiling salted water			
1 tablespoon salad oil			14
2 tablespoons lemon juice	2		
½ teaspoon dried oregano			
Salt and pepper			

Slice squash lengthwise and cook in the salted water about 8 minutes. Drain. Blend remaining ingredients and pour over hot squash. Let marinate about 5 minutes. Squash can then be lifted from dressing. Serves six.

Each serving of squash contains 4 grams of carbohydrate, 1 gram of protein, and 20 calories. This amount may be substituted for one group A vegetable exchange.

If dressing is eaten, count 45 calories per tablespoon and 5 grams of fat (or one fat exchange).

BAKED POTATO

	C	P	F
1 medium potato (100 grams) per serving	17	2	
½ cup dry cottage cheese	3	20	
¼ cup vegetable oil			50
¼ cup evaporated skim milk	6	4	
2 tablespoons chives, chopped	1		

Bake potato in usual manner. As soon as it is done split lengthwise and scoop out about a quarter or more of the potato and discard. (Those on weighed diets should weigh the potato after this has been removed and adjust calculations accordingly.) Put cottage cheese, oil, and milk in a blender and blend until smooth (or pass through a food mill if you have no blender). Use to replace discarded potato. Garnish with chives.

The cheese mixture contains 4 grams of fat (or about one fat exchange) and 35 calories *per tablespoon.* The carbohydrate and protein content can be disregarded, provided not more than 2 tablespoons are used.

COMMENT. When high-carbohydrate foods such as potato are served, an effort should be made to replace some of the starch with protein and/or fat. This permits the allowed carbohydrate to be taken in a more nutritious form.

Miscellaneous Vegetables

GREEN PEPPERS

	C	P	F
4 bell peppers, cut in quarters	14	5	
1 tablespoon unsaturated margarine			11
1 clove garlic			
1½ teaspoons salt			
⅛ teaspoon pepper			
1 teaspoon dried oregano			

Heat margarine in heavy skillet and add peppers and garlic; sauté 2 to 3 minutes. Sprinkle with seasoning; cover and simmer 10 minutes. Discard garlic. Serves four as a side dish.

One serving (four pieces) contains 4 grams of carbohydrate, 1 gram of protein, 3 grams of fat, 50 calories, and vitamins A and C. This amount may be substituted for one group A vegetable for one group B vegetable exchange.

STUFFED MUSHROOMS

	C	P	F
8 mushrooms (2 to 3 inches in diameter)	7	5	
1 teaspoon margarine, melted			4
2 green onions, chopped	4		
2 medium tomatoes, peeled and chopped	12	3	
½ teaspoon salt			
2 tablespoons bread crumbs	4	1	

Oil entire surface of mushrooms with melted margarine. Mix other ingredients, including chopped mushroom stems, and mound into mushroom caps. Place in flat pan and pour ¼ cup boiling water around caps. Bake in moderate oven (350°) for about 15 minutes.

Each mushroom contains 3 grams of carbohydrate, 1 gram of protein, 0.5 gram of fat, 20 calories, and vitamins A and C. This amount may be substituted for one group A vegetable exchange.

CELERY AND MUSHROOM STICKS

	C	P	F
½ cup raw mushrooms, chopped fine	4	3	
¼ cup green pepper, minced	1		
Celery sticks			

Blend mushrooms and green peppers with low-calorie mayonnaise and fill celery sticks. Serve on lettuce or as hors d'oeuvres.

Contains negligible carbohydrate, protein, and fat.

CHAPTER 8

Salads and Salad Dressings

Salads

A salad should accompany both lunch and dinner. Salads make splendid contributions of vitamins and minerals with little carbohydrate and few calories, unless rich dressings are used. They may be simple "finger salads" such as carrot sticks, radishes, etc., or elaborate molded creations. If fresh vegetables or fruits are used, they are all nutritious.

ASPARAGUS SALAD

	C	P	F
4 cups fresh raw asparagus tips	17	10	
4 to 6 cups lettuce leaves	8	4	
1 tablespoon Roquefort cheese		3	4
¼ cup vinegar	3		
Salt and black pepper			

Slice asparagus tips diagonally. Disperse cheese in vinegar and add salt and pepper to taste. Mix with asparagus. Yields six servings.

Each 1-cup serving contains 5 grams of carbohydrate, 3 grams of protein, 1 gram of fat, about 40 calories, and generous amounts of vitamin A. This amount may be substituted for one group A vegetable exchange.

MARINATED MUSHROOMS

	C	P	F
½ pound fresh mushrooms, sliced	8	6	
⅓ cup eschalot red wine vinegar	4		
1 teaspoon granular chicken bouillon			
1 teaspoon dried savory			
1 small green onion, sliced	2		
1 tomato	5	1	
1 tablespoon chopped parsley			
¼ cup water			

Mix and simmer all ingredients for 5 minutes. Drain and serve on crisp lettuce. Serves four.

A ¼-cup serving contains 5 grams of carbohydrate, 2 grams of protein, about 25 calories, and vitamins A, B, and C. This amount may be substituted for one group A vegetable exchange.

COMMENT. When instructions are given to drain away the liquid, as in the above recipe, it goes without saying that this liquid should be retained and used in some manner. Add to other marinades or soups, but do not discard.

COLE SLAW

	C	P	F
2 cups cabbage, finely shredded	9	3	
1 tablespoon onion, finely chopped	1		
2 teaspoons prepared mustard			
1 tablespoon special low-calorie mayonnaise	1	1	
¼ teaspoon salt			

Mix dressing ingredients and toss with cabbage. Garnish with toasted sesame seeds or toasted wheat germ. Serves four.

A ½-cup serving contains vitamin C, 3 grams of carbohydrate, and negligible protein and fat. This amount may be substituted for one group A vegetable exchange.

CUCUMBER MARINADE

	C	P	F
1 large cucumber, sliced crosswise	3	1	
1 small green onion with top	2		
½ teaspoon salt			
Pinch of black pepper			
Pinch of paprika			
2 drops Sweeta or other sweetener			
1 tablespoon vinegar	1		
¼ cup buttermilk	3	2	

Combine all ingredients and chill for 15 minutes. Drain before serving.

Contains negligible nutrients and calories. Need not be counted in daily diet calculations.

STUFFED TOMATOES

	C	P	F
4 large tomatoes	34	9	2
1 bunch water cress	1	1	
1 small cucumber, diced	2		
1 green onion, finely chopped	2		
½ teaspoon salt			
¼ teaspoon black pepper			

Remove tomato pulp and mix with other ingredients. Replace into tomato. Makes four servings.

Contains vitamins A, B, and C, 10 grams of carbohydrate, 2 grams of protein, and 50 calories per tomato. May be substituted for one group B vegetable exchange.

CHINESE TOMATO SALAD

	C	P	F
2 cups cabbage, finely chopped	9	3	
½ teaspoon salt			
2 medium tomatoes, finely chopped	12	3	
½ teaspoon dry mustard			
1 teaspoon water			
1 tablespoon soy sauce	2		
1 teaspoon sesame oil			5

Blend mustard, water, soy sauce, and sesame oil until smooth. Mix cabbage and tomatoes. Drizzle dressing over this. Serves six.

A ½-cup serving contains 4 grams of carbohydrate, negligible protein, 1 gram of fat, 25 calories, and vitamins A, B, and C. This amount may be substituted for one group A vegetable exchange.

MOLDED VEGETABLE SALAD

	C	P	F
1 package lemon gelatin dessert mix (sugar-free)		6	
2 tablespoons fresh lemon juice	2		
⅔ cup cabbage, chopped	3	1	
⅔ cup green pepper, chopped	3		
2 slices pimento			
2 cups boiling water			

Dissolve gelatin dessert mix in boiling water and stir until completely dissolved. Add chopped vegetables and chill. Slice when firm and serve on lettuce leaves with low-calorie dressing.

Contains large amounts of vitamins C and A; negligible carbohydrate, protein, and fat; and less than 20 calories per serving. It need not be included in diet calculations.

HAWAIIAN SALAD

	C	P	F
1 cup cucumbers, thinly sliced	5	1	
½ cup carrots, thinly sliced	7	1	
½ cup mushrooms, thinly sliced	3	2	
¼ teaspoon salt			
⅛ teaspoon ground ginger			
¼ cup white wine vinegar	3		
2 drops Sweeta or other sweetener			

Add salt to cucumbers and let stand for 10 minutes. Add remainder of ingredients. Chill in refrigerator for several hours. Drain well and serve on bed of lettuce. Makes four servings.

A ½-cup serving contains 5 grams of carbohydrate, 1 gram of protein, no fat, 25 calories, and vitamins A and C. This amount may be substituted for one group A vegetable exchange.

COMMENT. The mushrooms above are optional, but must be fresh if used. Calculations remain as they are if mushrooms are omitted.

Salad Dressings

The usual varieties of tossed or mixed green salads are permissible as free foods. It is only when they are combined with high-fat dressings that trouble begins. Included below are a few recipes for low-calorie dressings that can indeed be considered free if reasonable amounts are used. Leafy green salads have much to recommend them nutritionally, and it is desirable that diabetics, as well as other members of the family, have generous servings daily.

The flavor of mayonnaise comes primarily from the lemon and herbs used in it. Oils used in commercial mayonnaise are generally flavorless, and therefore a variety of thickened mixtures appropriately flavored can pass as mayonnaise in a pinch. None of the dressings included here are as good as real mayonnaise, nor indeed have I ever tasted a substitute that was as good as the real thing. They will, however, suffice if you must have a very restricted fat intake, count calories, or simply find yourself at dinner time with the day's allotment of fat used up and one meal left to go.

There are numerous kinds of packaged dressing mixes which are quite flavorful. They are marketed under various tradenames and sometimes have a special mixing bottle which can be purchased along with the dressing. The following combination can be used with any of the well-known brands available:

1 package salad dressing mix
2 tablespoons powdered pectin
3 tablespoons lemon juice
¾ cup water (or fill to the line marked "oil" if mixing kit is purchased)

These mixes contain negligible calories and nutrients but considerable flavor.

Occasionally I see a recipe for "low-fat" or "reducing" mayonnaise which uses mineral oil as a base. Mineral oil is not absorbed and therefore would lend itself to low-fat diets; however, there are good nutritional reasons why this kind of oil should not be used. Salad greens contain large amounts of vitamin A which will be lost along with the mineral oil. These greens may furnish the major part of vitamin A in the diet if it is extremely limited or if cooked greens are not eaten. Mineral oil mayonnaise cannot therefore be recommended.

LOW-FAT MAYONNAISE

	C	P	F
1 can (13 ounces) evaporated skim milk	38	27	1
½ teaspoon unflavored gelatin		1	
2 egg yolks		6	10
¾ teaspoon Sucaryl solution			
1½ teaspoons dry mustard			
1 teaspoon salt			
4 tablespoons fresh lemon juice	5		
½ teaspoon lemon peel, grated			

Reserve ¼ cup milk and sprinkle gelatin over the surface to soften. Heat remaining milk to scalding and add reserved portion containing gelatin. Remove from heat. Blend other ingredients until smooth and add milk mixture, 3 or 4 tablespoons at a time. Blend well after each addition. When all milk has been added, transfer to double boiler and cook gently, stirring constantly until mixture coats the spoon. Remove and add lemon juice and peel. Mixture will thicken as it cools.

Contains about 12 calories per tablespoon; 1 tablespoon may be used without counting any nutrient value in the diabetic's diet.

CHEESE DRESSING

Combine the preceding mayonnaise with either Roquefort or bleu cheese in the usual manner.

Allow 3 grams of protein and 4 grams of fat for *each* tablespoon of cheese. This is about 50 calories per tablespoon of cheese.

THOUSAND ISLAND DRESSING

	C	P	F
1 small dill pickle, chopped			
1 tablespoon catsup	4		
1 tablespoon chopped parsley			
½ cup low-fat mayonnaise	11	8	3

Combine ingredients. Makes about ¾ cup.

Entire amount contains 15 grams of carbohydrate, 8 grams of protein, and 3 grams of fat; 1 tablespoon contains negligible amounts.

FRESH HERB MAYONNAISE

	C	P	F
½ teaspoon dry mustard			
1 teaspoon salt			
2 tablespoons fresh parsley, minced			
1 tablespoon fresh chives, minced			
2 teaspoons dried tarragon, crumbled			
Juice of 1 lemon	5		
1 egg		7	6
¾ cup safflower or other unsaturated oil			150

Put first seven ingredients into a bowl and beat with wire whip until smooth. Add oil, 1 tablespoon at a time for about five additions. Beat well after each addition. Pour remaining oil in a thin stream, beating constantly. Omit tarragon, parsley, and chives for plain mayonnaise. Makes approximately 1 cup dressing.

Cut one head of Bibb lettuce into quarters. Spread cut surface lightly with herb mayonnaise and serve.

Each teaspoon of mayonnaise contains 3 grams of fat and 30 calories; 2 teaspoons may be substituted for one fat exchange.

FRENCH DRESSING

	C	P	F
4 tablespoons lemon juice	5		
2 tablespoons powdered pectin			
½ cup water			
¾ teaspoon salt			
¼ teaspoon paprika			
1 tablespoon catsup	4		

Combine ingredients. Shake well in a small jar and store in refrigerator.

Contains negligible nutrients and calories.

CHAPTER 9

"Free" Foods

Foods included in this chapter contain about 50 calories or less per serving and only small amounts of carbohydrate. A few recipes contain fat, and this must be included in your calculations if your diet is extremely fat-limited. In general, not more than one-half fat exchange (2.5 grams) is present in a single serving, however. These dishes should be used to add bulk, vitamins, and minerals in diets of 1200 calories or less. Such diets are difficult to balance even for experienced nutritionists, and the low-calorie, low-fat, and low-carbohydrate recipes presented throughout this book should be used frequently to supplement regular meal plans.

Although it is possible to purchase powders and cubes that make delicious meat stocks and bouillons, far more nutritious stocks can be made at home and stored if you have freezer space available. These are not inexpensive, but are more flavorful as well as more nutritious than the commercial products. It is probable that most persons will not prepare homemade stocks except for special dishes, since they do require more time than is needed for the commercially available mixes.

However, since diabetics must be vigilant about nutrients, recipes for homemade meat stocks are included here; commercial stocks can be substituted in all recipes.

The combination of meat stocks, vegetables, and fruits that make delicious, nutritious, low-calorie soups is limited only by the cook's imagination. Homemade stocks can make a valuable contribution, especially to diets of elderly people who have poor teeth and/or appetites. These older folk often do not drink milk and consequently have little or no source of calcium and phosphorus. The stock-based soups provide an easily digestible source of these minerals, plus a small amount of protein that is usually needed. If commercial bouillon is used, add 2 tablespoons of plain gelatin to each quart of liquid to equal the protein content of the homemade product.

CONSOMMÉ

	C	P	F
1 quart beef stock		16	
1 pinch dried majoram, thyme, and basil			
1 small clove garlic, crushed			
2 tablespoons chives, minced			
1½ teaspoons salt			

Simmer all ingredients 5 minutes. Top with small amount of grated lemon rind or very thin slice of lemon.

A 1-cup serving contains calcium, phosphorus, negligible carbohydrate, 4 grams of protein, no fat, and about 20 calories. This need not be counted on an exchange diet.

BEEF STOCK

3 pounds beef bones with some meat
3 quarts water
1 tablespoon vinegar

Brown bones slowly in heavy skillet or pot. When thoroughly brown on all sides, add water and vinegar. Simmer 3 hours or so. Strain stock into storage container and refrigerate. When cool, skim off fat and discard. The stock should have the consistency of a heavy gelatin solution at this point. Spoon into smaller containers and store in freezer until needed.

COMMENT. Our dietitian says that browning the bones doesn't add much flavor and is a big bother. She recommends dumping the fresh bones directly in the water. Browning is recommended more for color than for flavor and can be omitted if color is not important for your purposes.

MUSHROOM CONSOMMÉ

	C	P	F
1 quart beef stock		16	
½ pound mushrooms	8	6	
1½ teaspoons salt			

Bring stock to boiling. Add mushrooms and simmer for 3 to 4 minutes. If canned mushrooms are used, add canning liquid as well, but heat only to serving temperature. Makes about 5 cups.

A 1-cup serving contains calcium, iron, B vitamins, insignificant carbohydrate and fat, 4 grams of protein, and about 20 calories. This amount need not be counted on an exchange diet.

ONION SOUP

	C	P	F
1 quart beef stock		16	
1 teaspoon salt			
1 tablespoon cooking sherry			
4 large onions, thinly sliced			

Simmer stock and add sliced onions, salt, and sherry. Simmer 5 minutes. Strain and discard onions. Garnish with Parmesan cheese. Makes 4 cups.

Onions contain a significant amount of carbohydrate, and if left in must be counted in the daily intake. The above method gives considerable onion flavor without the added carbohydrate.

A 1-cup serving contains calcium, phosphorus, negligible carbohydrate, 4 grams of protein, no fat, and about 20 calories. It need not be counted on an exchange diet.

COMMENT. If you can afford the extra carbohydrate and wish to leave the onions in, count 10 grams of carbohydrate, 6 grams of protein, and 60 calories per cup.

ZUCCHINI SOUP

	C	P	F
1 quart beef stock		16	
1 medium zucchini, diced	10	3	
1½ teaspoons salt			

Boil stock and salt. Add zucchini and remove from heat. Let set for 5 minutes and serve. The zucchini should be quite crisp. Makes about 5 cups.

A 1-cup serving contains 2 grams of carbohydrate, 4 grams of protein, no fat, about 25 calories, calcium, phosphorus, and vitamins A and C. It need not be counted on an exchange diet.

COMMENT. Zucchini quickly becomes mushy if overcooked. This can be prevented by applying the salt directly to the squash for a few minutes prior to cooking. Cooking must still be brief, however. Do not freeze this soup as the flavor of zucchini is altered by freezing.

SPINACH BEEF SOUP

	C	P	F
1 quart beef stock		16	
1 large onion, quartered			
1 bunch spinach	4	3	
1 bunch parsley	1		
1 cup tomato purée	22	4	1

Add onion to stock and heat to boiling. Let cook for 3 to 4 minutes and remove onion; add purée, shredded spinach, and parsley leaves. The stems of both vegetables should be removed. Let simmer for 1 minute. Serve immediately. Makes 5 to 6 cups.

This delicious soup contains large amounts of vitamins A and B, calcium, phosphorus, and iron. A 1-cup serving has 4 grams of carbohydrate, 4 grams of protein, no fat, and about 30 calories. This amount counts as one group: A vegetable exchange.

COMMENT. Cooking time must be carefully controlled for spinach soups. If cooked too long (2 minutes is usually too long), the spinach loses its consistency and the flavor is altered. Other greens such as mustard, chard, and bok can take slightly more cooking, but not much more. The temptation in the above recipe is to leave the onion in longer. To do so results in too much onion taste. If the onion is cooked in the soup for only 3 to 4 minutes, it is not identifiable as such, and therefore the soup may be served safely on social occasions.

CHICKEN BOUILLON

1 quart chicken stock
1½ teaspoons salt (or more, depending on stock)
Pinch dried sage

Mix ingredients, heat to serving temperature, and garnish with unpeeled red apple.

A 1-cup serving contains calcium, phosphorus, negligible carbohydrate, 3 to 4 grams of protein, and negligible fat. It need not be counted on an exchange diet.

CHICKEN STOCK

4 to 5 pounds chicken backs and necks
½ cup onion, chopped
½ teaspoon dried thyme
Small bunch parsley
1 bay leaf
¼ teaspoon dried marjoram
3 quarts water

Mix all ingredients and simmer for 3 to 4 hours. Strain into storage container and cool in refrigerator. Remove fat and save for flavoring other dishes. Freeze stock for use in soups and other dishes.

Each quart contains approximately 16 grams of protein, along with calcium, phosphorus, and B vitamins.

COMMENT. If properly prepared, this stock should gel when refrigerated. It can therefore be used to prepare aspics or gelatin salads without the use of additional gelatin. The stock may not congeal after it has been frozen and should be fresh for use in this manner. It is considerably more nutritious than the stock prepared from packaged gelatin and bouillon cubes.

CHICKEN AND EGG SOUP

	C	P	F
1 quart chicken stock		16	
1½ teaspoons salt			
1 egg, well beaten		7	5

Simmer stock and add beaten egg in a thin stream while stirring the soup quickly. Remove from heat and serve immediately.

A 1-cup serving contains calcium, phosphorus, iron, small amounts of vitamins A and E, 5 grams of protein, 1 gram of fat, and about 30 calories. It need not be counted on an exchange diet.

COMMENT. For low-fat diets, substitute 2 egg whites and a few drops of yellow food coloring for the whole egg. This eliminates the fat entirely and decreases the calories to 20 per serving. For higher-fat diets, add extra oil to individual servings. Increase fat count by 5 grams per teaspoon added and calories by 45 for each teaspoon added.

CHICKEN CUCUMBER SOUP

	C	P	F
1 quart chicken stock		16	
1½ teaspoons salt			
2 large cucumbers, diced	7	2	

Sprinkle salt over cucumbers and let sit for 15 minutes. Simmer stock and add cucumbers. Turn off heat and let sit for 5 more minutes. Cucumbers should still be crisp. Garnish with grated orange peel. Makes 5 to 6 cups.

A 1-cup serving contains negligible carbohydrate, 4 grams of protein, no fat, and about 20 calories. It need not be counted on an exchange diet.

CHICKEN MUSHROOM SOUP

	C	P	F
1 quart chicken stock		16	
1½ teaspoons salt			
½ pound fresh mushrooms	8	6	

Simmer stock and add mushrooms and salt. Simmer 4 to 5 minutes and serve. If canned mushrooms are used, add liquid and heat only to serving temperature. Makes 5 cups.

Each 1-cup serving contains calcium, phosphorus, negligible carbohydrate, 4 grams of protein, negligible fat, and about 20 calories. It need not be counted on an exchange diet.

SPINACH SOUP

	C	P	F
1 quart water			
1½ teaspoons salt			
¼ teaspoon sugar	1		
2 bunches (about ½ pound) spinach	8	7	
2 teaspoons sesame oil			10

Bring water to boiling and add greens (chard, mustard, or turnip greens can be used, but spinach is very good), salt, and sugar. Boil 2 minutes. Remove from heat. Add ½ teaspoon sesame oil to *each* serving.

A 1-cup serving contains vitamins A, B, and C, negligible carbohydrate and protein, and 2.5 grams of fat. The fat can be omitted, but with some detriment to the flavor. If fat is included, a 1-cup serving yields about 35 calories and may be substituted for one-half fat exchange and one group A vegetable exchange.

COMMENT. If your diet requires larger amounts of fat, this soup can easily accommodate more than is recommended above. Each cup can carry 1 to 2 teaspoons. Don't forget to allow for the extra calories and to include the extra fat exchanges if you add more.

TOMATO SQUASH SOUP

	C	P	F
2 cups tomatoes (preferably fresh)	16	4	
½ cup yellow squash, diced	3	1	
¼ teaspoon dried dill weed			

Combine ingredients. Simmer 5 to 8 minutes (squash should still be crisp). Add salt to taste. Makes four servings of ½ cup each.

A ½-cup serving contains 5 grams of carbohydrate, 1 gram of protein, 25 calories, and significant amounts of vitamins A, B, and C. One serving may be substituted for one group A vegetable exchange.

CHAPTER 10

Emergency Diets

A time inevitably comes when the regular diet cannot be consumed. The occasion may be a case of the flu, dental work, or simply poor appetite. The diabetic must keep his intake fairly constant or serious complications may arise. If vomiting or diarrhea occurs, supplemental feedings are necessary, and although management of these illnesses must be supervised by a physician, you should know of liquid formulas that can be taken under these circumstances. An adult needs at least 100 grams of carbohydrate and 60 grams of protein daily when ill. The suggestions that follow can be supplemented with fruit juices, ginger ale, 7-Up, and similar beverages. Generally citrus juices are not well tolerated when nausea is present, and juices such as blackberry and cranberry are useful to have on hand for such occasions. Recipes for two useful drinks, Fruit Float and Peach Float, are given in Chapter 6.

LIQUID DIET NO. 1

	C	P	F
1 quart whole milk	48	34	34
2 eggs, well beaten		14	12
½ can (6 ounces) orange juice concentrate	66	4	
½ cup powdered skim milk	16	11	

Mix well in blender or jar and use as frequent small feedings. Total volume is 1¼ quarts.

Entire recipe contains approximately 1200 calories, 130 grams of carbohydrate, 63 grams of protein, and 46 grams of fat. This may be substituted for four bread, six meat, two whole milk, and five fruit exchanges.

LIQUID DIET NO. 2

	C	P	F
1½ quarts water			
2 cups powdered skim milk	62	43	1
2 eggs		14	12
½ cup orange juice	12	1	

Mix well and serve in divided portions. Total volume is 1¾ quarts.

Entire recipe contains 650 calories, 75 grams of carbohydrate, 60 grams of protein, and 12 grams of fat. This may be substituted for five skim milk, two meat, and one fruit exchanges.

COMMENT. Skim milk (1½ quarts) can be substituted for the powdered milk and water without unduly affecting the calculations.

LIQUID DIET NO. 3

	C	P	F	Alcohol
1 quart whole milk	48	34	34	
1 can (6 ounces) evaporated milk	18	13	14	
2 tablespoons brandy or bourbon				10.5
2 eggs		14	12	
½ cup vanilla ice cream	16	3	8	
Nutmeg to taste				

Blend well and serve in divided portions.

Entire recipe contains 1270 calories (73 calories are from alcohol), 82 grams of carbohydrate, 64 grams of protein, and 68 grams of fat. This may be substituted for five and one-half milk, two meat, one bread, and one fat exchanges.

LIQUID DIET NO. 4

	C	P	F
1 quart chicken or beef stock		16	
2 tablespoons plain gelatin		17	
1 cup tomato juice	10	2	
Salt to taste			

Soften gelatin in a small amount of cold stock; then heat to boiling. Add tomato juice and salt.

This can be served as a clear soup along with one of the other liquid diets. It does not fulfill an entire day's nutritional requirements alone.

Entire recipe contains 180 calories, 10 grams of carbohydrate, and 35 grams of protein.

Additional carbohydrate can be taken as crackers or toast along with this if it is served as a soup. The above calculations are made on the basis of homemade stock. If bouillon cubes are used, increase added gelatin to 4 tablespoons and leave calculations as they appear.

I once scolded a German girl for feeding her small son only oatmeal for breakfast. She revealed the following combination to me and I readily admitted that her version of oatmeal was a satisfactory breakfast. I have since recommended it many times to young and old alike, who prefer cereals to more substantial breakfast fare.

SPECIAL OATMEAL

	C	P	F
½ cup (40 grams) oatmeal	27	6	3
1 cup water			
2 tablespoons (15 grams) raisins	10		
½ cup evaporated skim milk	12	8	
1 egg, well beaten		7	6

Use salted water to cook oatmeal and raisins in usual way. Combine milk and egg and add to cooked oatmeal. Remove from heat and stir until well mixed. Cover and let set for 5 minutes. Add liquid sweetener to taste and sprinkle with cinnamon. Makes one large or two small servings.

Entire amount contains 49 grams of carbohydrate, 21 grams of protein, 9 grams of fat, and 361 calories. This may be substituted for one skim milk, one meat, one fruit, and two bread exchanges.

COMMENT. If your allowance of saturated fat is extremely restricted, omit the egg yolk and use instead 2 egg whites and 1 teaspoon unsaturated margarine.

ENRICHED MILK TOAST

	C	P	F
1 slice dry whole-wheat toast	15	2	
1 cup whole milk	12	8	10
1 egg, well beaten		7	6
Dash of nutmeg			

Combine milk and egg; heat gently or in double boiler until steaming hot. Do not boil. Place toast in flat-bottom bowl and add hot milk and egg mixture. Sprinkle with nutmeg.

This contains 27 grams of carbohydrate, 17 grams of protein, 16 grams of fat, and 320 calories. It may be substituted for one bread, one whole milk, and one meat exchanges.

COMMENT. This can also be used for fussy breakfast eaters. It is a painless way to get an egg down a child who temporarily refuses it.

PLAIN CUSTARD

	C	P	F
2 teaspoons Sucaryl or equivalent amount of other sweetener			
½ cup powdered skim milk	6	4	
Pinch of salt			
½ cup evaporated skim milk	12	8	
3 eggs (or 3 egg whites and 3 teaspoons oil for unsaturated-fat diet)		21	18
1 teaspoon vanilla			
1½ cups liquid skim milk	18	12	

Mix all ingredients except liquid skim milk, beat until smooth, and add skim milk. Pour into four individual baking dishes and sprinkle with nutmeg. Measure or weigh so dishes are of equal volume. Set baking dishes in pan with small amount of water and bake at 325° until custard is well set on outside, but still soft in center.

Each serving contains 9 grams of carbohydrate, 11 grams of protein, 5 grams of fat, and 125 calories. This may be substituted for one meat and three-quarters skim milk exchanges.

BLACKBERRY GELATIN

	C	P	F
2 cups blackberry juice (canned or prepared from fresh berries, unsweetened)	36		
1 package (1 tablespoon) plain gelatin		8	
Artificial sweetener			

Heat 1 cup blackberry juice to boiling and use to dissolve gelatin. When completely dissolved, add remaining juice and artificial sweetener to taste. Measure into four equal servings.

Each serving contains 9 grams of carbohydrate, 2 grams of protein, and 44 calories. It may be substituted for one fruit exchange.

COMMENT. This is especially kind to upset stomachs and is often tolerated when other fruits and juices are not. Cranberry juice can be substituted for the blackberry juice without detriment to flavor. Cranberry juice can be purchased in an artificially sweetened form, and if that is used, of course, omit additional sweetener. Two cups dietetic cranberry juice contain 8 grams of carbohydrate. A ½-cup serving of this cranberry gelatin can be taken without counting any food value.

GELATIN DESSERT

	C	P	F
1 package D-Zerta (or other comparable product) strawberry gelatin		6	
1 cup boiling water			
1 cup cool water			
1 cup fresh strawberries, whole	11		

Dissolve gelatin in boiling water. Add cold water. Measure into four equal portions. Weigh or measure strawberries and divide into four equal portions; add to gelatin and refrigerate until set. This is a very pretty dish and will tempt timid appetites.

Each portion contains 3 grams of carbohydrate, 1.5 grams of protein, and 18 calories. This may be substituted for one-third fruit exchange.

CHAPTER 11

Revising and Creating Recipes

Most new recipes are created in the test kitchens of companies that have products to sell. Many of these products are excellent, as are the recipes that promote their use. However, some leave much to be desired nutritionally. It is wise to look at new recipes with nutrition in mind and attempt to alter them, if necessary, to increase their value. This is especially important for the diabetic. A new recipe for use in a family with a diabetic member should be evaluated in terms of its content of sugar, total carbohydrate, fat, and vitamins and minerals, and altered as necessary.

ALTERING SUGAR CONTENT

A recipe's sugar content is perhaps its most important feature, since any recipe requiring more than a tablespoon of sugar has to be altered for a diabetic. The various artificial sweeteners have already been considered in Chapter 4. These substances may be used in many recipes but, unfortunately, are not suitable for many others. All companies that sell artificial sweeteners publish small cookbooks that are free for the asking. These booklets contain recipes for the kinds of dishes for which the manufacturer's product is suitable. Compare your recipe with theirs, and if you find a similar one, chances are that yours can be adapted successfully. Most of these manufacturers retain consulting home economists or dietitians who will render opinion on recipes submitted to them.

ALTERING CARBOHYDRATE CONTENT

Not only sugar but total carbohydrate must be considered in new recipes. If the basic materials are flour, potatoes, macaroni, noodles, or similar foods, the carbohydrate content is high. This does not mean that the dish cannot be used, but rather that it must be used instead of bread or in very limited quantities. If it is to be substituted for bread, consider the vitamin and mineral content as well. If it does not compare favorably with the content of whole-grain bread, then either alter the recipe so that it does, or better, discard the recipe. As discussed earlier, it is often possible to increase both the vitamin and the mineral content of flours and flour products by adding brewer's yeast to the flour before sifting and measuring. Be sure the flavor of the yeast will be compatible if you are adding much. The amounts of the various vitamins you are adding can be calculated from the information on the yeast box, if you are at all talented in mathematics. Portions of flour used in pie crusts, pastries, etc., can be replaced with soy flour. This reduces the carbohydrate content and raises the protein level. A light hand is sometimes necessary, however, for if much soy flour is used you may need help to lift the result. A cake baked of even half soy flour is a very heavy cake. On the other hand, soy flour does not detract from the breads one expects to have a heavy texture, and pie crust made entirely from soy flour is respectable indeed.

ALTERING FAT CONTENT

Not only total fat content but kind of fat must be evaluated. One can almost always replace saturated with unsaturated fat with little detriment to the final result. Egg yolk can be replaced by another egg white. If the egg color is needed, yellow food coloring can be added. Unsaturated margarine can be substituted for butter, low-fat yogurt for sour cream, Neufchâtel cheese for cream cheese (the former contains saturated fat, but less of it). If the total fat content must be reduced, gradually cut down the total amount until the minimal acceptable level has been reached. If you do this each time you prepare a recipe, you can greatly reduce the total amount in many recipes. The low-calorie margarines now on the market help in this regard. Unfortunately, they are not really suitable for frying foods, owing to the thickening agents in them, but they make a very tasty substitute for butter on bread, pancakes, etc. In general, they contain about half as much fat as regular margarine.

ALTERING VITAMIN AND MINERAL CONTENT

Almost any published recipe is the better for this kind of alteration. Some recipes seem to be calculated to give the least nutrition possible! Improvements can be effected by saving the cooking liquid for use in other dishes, substituting a nutritious meat stock for the liquid specified, using less volume of liquid, avoiding soaking and peeling vegetables and fruits, shortening the cooking time, and substituting more nutritious ingredients for some of those specified (for example, whole-grain for refined flour, milk for water).

CALCULATING NUTRITIONAL CONTENT

To calculate the nutritional content of a recipe, you need a good set of food content lists, similar to but more complete than those in Table 2 of this book. You can obtain a set of food content lists from your county agent or from the superintendent of documents, U.S. Government Printing Office, Washington, D.C., 20402. Single copies are free. Ask for House and Garden Bulletin No. 72, *Nutritive Value of Foods*. Perhaps your local home economist will explain the calculation procedure to you or suggest other publications that will.

Use salted water to cook oatmeal and raisins in usual way. Combine milk and egg and add to cooked oatmeal. Remove from heat and stir until well mixed. Cover and let set for 5 minutes. Add liquid sweetener to taste and sprinkle with cinnamon. Makes one large or two small servings.

Entire amount contains 49 grams of carbohydrate, 21 grams of protein, 9 grams of fat, and 361 calories. This may be substituted for one skim milk, one meat, one fruit, and two bread exchanges.

COMMENT. If your allowance of saturated fat is extremely restricted, omit the egg yolk and use instead 2 egg whites and 1 teaspoon unsaturated margarine.

ENRICHED MILK TOAST

	C	P	F
1 slice dry whole-wheat toast	15	2	
1 cup whole milk	12	8	10
1 egg, well beaten		7	6
Dash of nutmeg			

Combine milk and egg; heat gently or in double boiler until steaming hot. Do not boil. Place toast in flat-bottom bowl and add hot milk and egg mixture. Sprinkle with nutmeg.

This contains 27 grams of carbohydrate, 17 grams of protein, 16 grams of fat, and 320 calories. It may be substituted for one bread, one whole milk, and one meat exchanges.

COMMENT. This can also be used for fussy breakfast eaters. It is a painless way to get an egg down a child who temporarily refuses it.

PLAIN CUSTARD

	C	P	F
2 teaspoons Sucaryl or equivalent amount of other sweetener			
½ cup powdered skim milk	6	4	
Pinch of salt			
½ cup evaporated skim milk	12	8	
3 eggs (or 3 egg whites and 3 teaspoons oil for unsaturated-fat diet)		21	18
1 teaspoon vanilla			
1½ cups liquid skim milk	18	12	

Mix all ingredients except liquid skim milk, beat until smooth, and add skim milk. Pour into four individual baking dishes and sprinkle with nutmeg. Measure or weigh so dishes are of equal volume. Set baking dishes in pan with small amount of water and bake at 325° until custard is well set on outside, but still soft in center.

Each serving contains 9 grams of carbohydrate, 11 grams of protein, 5 grams of fat, and 125 calories. This may be substituted for one meat and three-quarters skim milk exchanges.

BLACKBERRY GELATIN

	C	P	F
2 cups blackberry juice (canned or prepared from fresh berries, unsweetened)	36		
1 package (1 tablespoon) plain gelatin		8	
Artificial sweetener			

Heat 1 cup blackberry juice to boiling and use to dissolve gelatin. When completely dissolved, add remaining juice and artificial sweetener to taste. Measure into four equal servings.

Each serving contains 9 grams of carbohydrate, 2 grams of protein, and 44 calories. It may be substituted for one fruit exchange.

COMMENT. This is especially kind to upset stomachs and is often tolerated when other fruits and juices are not. Cranberry juice can be substituted for the blackberry juice without detriment

The several examples of nutrition calculations presented earlier in this book should be referred to for exercises. As another example, let us consider the following recipe:

BISCUITS

2 cups flour
3 teaspoons baking powder
1 teaspoon salt
⅓ cup butter
¾ cup whole milk

We note that the basic materials are high in carbohydrate and fat content. This can be ameliorated by using whole-wheat flour to provide more vitamins and minerals per gram of carbohydrate and by substituting unsaturated for the saturated fat and skim milk for the whole milk. We now consult the food content lists for the nutritional content of the ingredients. The 2 cups of whole-wheat flour contain 170 grams of carbohydrate, 32 grams of protein, and 4 grams of fat. The ⅓ cup of unsaturated margarine (substituted for the butter) contains 61 grams of fat, and negligible carbohydrate and protein. The ¾ cup of skim milk contains 9 grams of carbohydrate, 6 grams of protein, and no fat. The seasonings can be disregarded in this case. Now we add the figures for each ingredient to obtain the total contained in the recipe:

	C	P	F
Flour	170	32	4
Margarine			61
Milk	9	6	
Total	179	38	65

This amount makes one dozen biscuits. If we divide the above totals by the total number of biscuits, we can determine the nutritional content of each biscuit. This, of course, assumes that the biscuits are equal in size, and care must be taken in this regard. Each biscuit has the following nutritional content:

179/12 = 15 grams of carbohydrate
38/12 = 3 grams of protein
65/12 = 5 grams of fat

Each biscuit equals one bread exchange and one fat exchange.

To calculate the calorie content, remember that carbohydrate and protein each contain 4 calories per gram and fat contains 9 calories per gram. The necessary mathematics are as follows:

$15 \times 4 = 60$ carbohydrate calories
$3 \times 4 = 12$ protein calories
$5 \times 9 = 45$ fat calories

Thus there is a total of 117 calories per biscuit. If extra fat is used to "butter" the biscuit, it must be counted in addition.

Although these mechanics seem complicated to the beginner, if used frequently they will become second nature. When the method is mastered completely, the nutritional content of any recipe can be determined and the new dish introduced with no detriment to the diabetic diet.

Appendix

AFFILIATE DIABETES ASSOCIATIONS AND COMPONENT ORGANIZATIONS

The American Diabetes Association, a voluntary health agency, is composed of 53 affiliate associations and 74 component organizations (nonprofessional) established throughout the United States. These are listed in the following pages. The purpose of these affiliates is to implement the aims of the national association in furthering educational and research services for physicians and other interested individuals, to offer a wide program of appropriate activities to people with diabetes mellitus and to their parents and families, and to conduct public education programs directed toward diabetes detection.

It is well established that most persons with diabetes can share in many benefits by membership in these organizations. Through attendance at the regular meetings scheduled during the year, the individual with diabetes may hear medical lectures and may participate in group discussions, dietetic demonstrations, and a wide range of activities planned under competent medical guidance.

Special programs of social events are frequently presented, including luncheons, picnics, card parties, and other forms of group entertainment. Certain affiliates offer counseling on insurance and on vocational and employment problems; camping facilities for children with diabetes are provided in most parts of the country.

Among the rewarding aspects of participating in an affiliate association is the deep personal satisfaction that can result from community service and from contributing to program planning.

Anyone with diabetes, seeking advice and guidance or interested in any phase of the condition and its control, is invited to communicate with the affiliate or any of its branches in his area.

ALABAMA

Alabama Diabetes Association, Inc.*
1137 Del Ray Drive
Birmingham, Alabama 35213
Telephone: 592-0562 or 324-6581, Ext. 453

Birmingham Lay Diabetes Society
2600 Willow Brook Lane
Birmingham, Alabama 35226
Telephone: 822-5295, 592-0081, or 785-8031

Etowah County Lay Society
P.O. Box 164
Gadsden, Alabama 35902
Telephone: 547-8609

Mobile Lay Society
4308 Cedars Avenue
Mobile, Alabama 36608
Telephone: 342-7424

Tuscaloosa Lay Society
Y.M.C.A.
Tuscaloosa, Alabama 35403
Telephone: 758-5503

CALIFORNIA

Alameda-Contra Costa Diabetes Association, Inc.
P.O. Box 11208
Oakland, California 94611
Telephone: 893-5480

Fresno County Diabetes Association, Inc.*
P.O. Box 4133
Fresno, California 93744
Telephone: 237-0123

Diabetes Association of Southern California, Inc.
2007 Wilshire Boulevard, Suite 901
Los Angeles, California 90057
Telephone: 483-3740

Chapters in Southern California:
Central
Glendale-Foothill
Highland Park
Long Beach
Orange County
Pomona Valley
Riverside County
San Bernardino County
San Diego County
San Fernando Valley
San Gabriel Valley
South Bay
Ventura County
Westside

(For information about the activities of the above chapters, write or telephone the office of the Diabetes Association of Southern California, Inc.)

San Francisco Diabetes Association, Inc.*
6200 Geary Boulevard, Suite 106
San Francisco, California 94121
Telephone: 221-1441

COLORADO

Colorado Diabetes Association, Inc.*
1375 Delaware Street
Denver, Colorado 80204
Telephone: 623-2221

Boulder Lay Society
4570 Sioux Drive
Boulder, Colorado 80302
Telephone: 442-4846

CONNECTICUT

Connecticut Diabetes Association, Inc.
79 Elm Street, Room 203
Hartford, Connecticut 06115
Telephone: 527-6341, Ext. 817

* Indicates affiliate association having a component lay society.

List received January 1969 from the American Diabetes Association, 18 East 48th Street, New York, N.Y. 10017.

DELAWARE

Delaware Diabetes Association, Inc.*
1925 Lovering Avenue
Wilmington, Delaware 19806
Telephone: 656-0030

DISTRICT OF COLUMBIA

Diabetes Association of the District of Columbia, Inc.*
800 Pershing Drive
Silver Spring, Maryland 20910
Telephone: 588-4220

FLORIDA

Florida Diabetes Association, Inc.*
1910 Riverside Drive East
Bradenton, Florida 33505
Telephone: 746-7071

Alachua County Lay Society
J. Hillis Miller Health Center
Gainesville, Florida 32601
Telephone: 376-3211, Ext. 5113

Brevard County Lay Society
2415 Riviera Drive
Titusville, Florida 32780
Telephone: 267-0815

Duval County Lay Society
1304 North Sixth Avenue
Jacksonville Beach, Florida 32050
Telephone: 246-2086

Greater Miami Lay Society
8751 S.W. 192nd Street
Miami, Florida 33157
Telephone: 238-5836

Hillsborough County Lay Society
4417 Ballas Point Road
Tampa, Florida 33611
Telephone: 839-1055

Lake County Lay Society
114 Euclid Avenue
Leesburg, Florida 32748
Telephone: 787-4846

Manatee County Lay Society
1910 Riverside Drive, East
Bradenton, Florida 33505
Telephone: 746-7071

Orange County Lay Society
515 North Dollins Avenue
Orlando, Florida 32805
Telephone: 425-8486

Pinellas County Lay Society
478-25th Avenue, North
St. Petersburg, Florida 33704
Telephone: 894-1763

Polk County Lay Society
2032 Leisure Drive, N.W.
Winter Haven, Florida 33880
Telephone: 293-8775

Sarasota County Lay Society
3737 Nogales Drive
Sarasota, Florida 33580
Telephone: 355-3902

Volusia County Lay Society
Halifax Senior Citizens Center
524 South Beach Street
Daytona Beach, Florida 32018
Telephone: 252-9970

GEORGIA

Georgia Diabetes Association, Inc.*
875 West Peachtree Street, N.E.
Atlanta, Georgia 30309
Telephone: 874-5875

Columbus Lay Society
2000 Hilton Avenue
Columbus, Georgia 31906
Telephone: 324-2418

Diabetes Association of Atlanta, Inc.*
875 West Peachtree Street, N.E.
Atlanta, Georgia 30309
Telephone: Day, 874-5875; evening, 753-1437

ILLINOIS

Diabetes Association of Greater Chicago, Inc.*
620 North Michigan Avenue
Chicago, Illinois 60641
Telephone: 943-8668

* Indicates affiliate association having a component lay society.

Downstate Illinois Diabetes Association, Inc.
100 West Miller Street
Springfield, Illinois 62702
Telephone: 544-9881

INDIANA

Indianapolis Diabetes Association, Inc.*
810 Hume Mansur Building
Indianapolis, Indiana 46204
Telephone: 639-1111

KANSAS

See under Kansas City, Missouri

KENTUCKY

Kentucky Diabetes Association, Inc.*
3337 Medical Arts Building
Louisville, Kentucky 40217
Telephone: 458-3259

Jefferson County Lay Society
922 Parkway Drive
Louisville, Kentucky 40217
Telephone: 637-7876

LOUISIANA

Diabetes Association of Louisiana, Inc.*
1130 Louisiana Avenue
Shreveport, Louisiana 71102
Telephone: 422-2158

Baton Rouge Area Lay Society
2642 Ray Weiland
Baker, Louisiana 70714
Telephone: 755-1629

MAINE

See under Massachusetts

MARYLAND

Maryland Diabetes Association, Inc.*
Baltimore Federal Building
Fayette and St. Paul Streets
Baltimore, Maryland 21202
Telephone: 685-2257

Baltimore Lay Society
Baltimore Federal Building
Fayette and St. Paul Streets
Baltimore, Maryland 21202
Telephone: 685-2257

MASSACHUSETTS

New England Diabetes Association, Inc.
7 Kenilworth Circle
Wellesley, Massachusetts 02181
Telephone: 223-7450

MICHIGAN

Michigan Diabetes Association, Inc.*
6131 West Outer Drive
Detroit, Michigan 48235
Telephone: 342-9333

(For information about the activities of the lay societies write or telephone the office of the Michigan Diabetes Association, Inc.)

MINNESOTA

Twin Cities Diabetes Association, Inc.*
205 Deerwood Lane
Minneapolis, Minnesota 55427
Telephone: 545-0148

MISSISSIPPI

Diabetes Association of Mississippi, Inc.
415 South 28th Avenue
Hattiesburg, Mississippi 39401
Telephone: 584-8421

* Indicates affiliate association having a component lay society.

MISSOURI

Kansas City Clinical Diabetes Association, Inc.* and Diabetes Lay Society of Greater Kansas City
P.O. Box 8463
Kansas City, Missouri 64114
Telephone: EMerson 3-2816

Missouri State Diabetes Association, Inc.
4620 J. C. Nichols Parkway
Kansas City, Missouri 64112
Telephone: LOgan 1-8166

St. Louis Diabetes Association, Inc.*
3839 Lindell Boulevard
St. Louis, Missouri 63108
Telephone: 533-4143

NEBRASKA

Nebraska Diabetes Association, Inc.*
510 Faculty Building
2305 South 10th Street
Omaha, Nebraska 68108
Telephone: 348-2522

Greater Lincoln Lay Society
1026 "K" Street, Apt. 1
Lincoln, Nebraska 68508
Telephone: 477-2600

NEW HAMPSHIRE

See under Massachusetts

NEW JERSEY

New Jersey Diabetes Association, Inc.*
317 Belleville Avenue
Bloomfield, New Jersey 07003

New Jersey Diabetes League
(Lay Society of the New Jersey Diabetes Association)
60 Edgemont Road
Montclair, New Jersey 07042
Telephone: 744-7414

See under Pennsylvania for Gloucester County, N.J. Lay Society

NEW YORK

Buffalo Diabetes Association, Inc.*
50 High Street
Buffalo, New York 14203
Telephone: 886-3123

New York Diabetes Association, Inc.*
104 East 40th Street
New York, New York 10016
Telephone: OXford 7-7760

New York Lay Society
104 East 40th Street
New York, New York 10016
Telephone: OXford 7-7760

Nassau County Diabetes Lay Society
134 Union Avenue
Lynbrook, New York 11563
Telephone: LYnbrook 9-9759

Niagara Falls Diabetes Association, Inc.*
817 Main Street
Niagara Falls, New York 14301
Telephone: 284-9913

Northeastern New York Diabetes Association, Inc*
921 Nott Street
Schenectady, New York 12308
Telephone: 374-0151

Schenectady Area Lay Society
2857 Consaul Road
Schenectady, New York 12304
Telephone: 346-1973

Rochester Regional Diabetes Association, Inc.
1351 Mount Hope Avenue
Rochester, New York 14620
Telephone: 271-4220

Westchester Diabetes Association, Inc.*
4 Brambach Avenue
Scarsdale, New York 10583
Telephone: SCarsdale 3-4156

NORTH CAROLINA

North Carolina Diabetes Association, Inc.
The Nalle Clinic
1350 South Kings Drive
Charlotte, North Carolina 28207
Telephone: 334-5531

* Indicates affiliate association having a component lay society.

NORTH DAKOTA

North Dakota Diabetes Association, Inc.
221 South Fourth Street
Grand Forks, North Dakota 58201
Telephone: 775-8121

OHIO

Diabetes Association of the Cincinnati Area, Inc.*
2400 Reading Road
Cincinnati, Ohio 45202
Telephone: 721-3160, Ext. 231

Dayton Area Diabetes Association, Inc.*
7424 Eagle Creek Drive
Dayton, Ohio 45459
Telephone: 433-4657

Summit County Diabetes Association, Inc.
326 Locust Street
Akron, Ohio 44302
Telephone: 762-8831

Toledo Diabetes Association, Inc.*
1215 Marmion Avenue
Toledo, Ohio 43607
Telephone: 536-3119

OKLAHOMA

Oklahoma Diabetes Association, Inc.
2021 South Lewis
Tulsa, Oklahoma 74104
Telephone: RI 7-4310

OREGON

Diabetes Association of Oregon, Inc.
2222 N.W. Lovejoy
Portland, Oregon 97210
Telephone: 227-2571

PENNSYLVANIA

Delware Valley Diabetes Association, Inc.*
1832 Spruce Street
Philadelphia, Pennsylvania 19103
Telephone: PE 5-2541

Gloucester County Lay Society
36 Martanna Avenue
Deptford, New Jersey 08096
Telephone: 227-1258

Lehigh Valley Diabetes Association, Inc.*
3075 Lindberg Avenue
Allentown, Pennsylvania 18103
Telephone: 434-0069

Pittsburgh Diabetes Association, Inc.*
200 Ross Street
Pittsburgh, Pennsylvania 15219
Telephone: 261-6010, Ext. 306

Reading Diabetes Association, Inc.*
1800 Olive Street
Reading, Pennsylvania 19604
Telephone: 373-6244

RHODE ISLAND

See under Massachusetts

TENNESSEE

Tennessee Diabetes Association, Inc.*
188 South Bellevue
Memphis, Tennessee 38104
Telephone: 276-2791

Memphis Lay Society
1850 Poplar Estates Parkway
Germantown, Tennessee 38038
Telephone: 884-7401

Nashville Lay Society
Aladdin Industries
705 Murfreesboro Road
Nashville, Tennessee 37210
Telephone: 242-3411, Ext. 294

TEXAS

Texas Diabetes Association, Inc.
Veterans Administration Hospital
4500 South Lancaster Road
Dallas, Texas 75216

* Indicates affiliate association having a component lay society.

Dallas Diabetes Association, Inc.
2909 Maple Avenue
Dallas, Texas 75201
Telephone: RIverside 7-2185

South Texas Diabetes Association, Inc.*
P. O. Box 148
Friendswood, Texas 77546
Telephone: 482-1001

VERMONT

See under Massachusetts

VIRGINIA

Virginia Diabetes Association, Inc.*
608 Medical Tower
Norfolk, Virginia 23507
Telephone: MAdison 2-6431

Piedmont Area Lay Society
P. O. Box 1211
Charlottesville, Virginia 22902
Telephone: 296-6974

Richmond Area Lay Society
P. O. Box 7191
Richmond, Virginia 23221
Telephone: 270-1883

WASHINGTON

Washington Diabetes Association, Inc.*
1000 Seneca Street
Seattle, Washington 98101
Telephone: MAin 4-5240

WEST VIRGINIA

West Virginia Diabetes Association, Inc.*
1033 Forest Road
Charleston, West Virginia 25314
Telephone: 343-2743

Charleston Lay Society
P. O. Box 174
Charleston, West Virginia 25314
Telephone: 727-4686

WISCONSIN

Wisconsin Diabetes Association, Inc.*
225 East Michigan Street
Milwaukee, Wisconsin 53202
Telephone: 276-6447

Milwaukee Lay Society
1723 Alta Vista Avenue
Milwaukee, Wisconsin 53213
Telephone: 453-0125

* Indicates affiliate association having a component lay society.

Index